THE WARRIOR KING

Doris Leslie

SAPERE
BOOKS

THE WARRIOR KING

Published by Sapere Books.

24 Trafalgar Road, Ilkley, LS29 8HH

saperebooks.com

ISBN: 978-0-85495-053-9

To the memory of my beloved husband,
Sir Walter Fergusson Hannay,
and of all the Clan Hannay Society
whose ancestor fought with and for
Richard the Lion Heart in the Third Crusade.
Per Ardua ad Alta

FOREWORD

In writing this reign of Richard Plantagenet and the Third Crusade I have endeavoured to keep strictly to fact based upon the accounts of eyewitnesses; but these are not always reliable. However, neither the characters nor any excerpts from letters or verses quoted in translation from the Norman French are fictitious.

Among the authorities past and present who have aided my research, I am deeply indebted to:

Ambroise, *L'Estoire de la guerre sainte,* Gaston, Paris 1897;

William Aytoun, *The Life and Times of Richard I,* 1840;

Kate Norgate, *Richard The Lion Heart,* 1924;

Philip Henderson, *Richard Coeur de Lion,* 1958;

John Gillingham, *The Life and Times of Richard I,* 1973.

And finally to Mrs Barbara Cheeseman for her excellent typing and editing of my manuscript.

DORIS LESLIE

ONE

The old king was dying. Grouped around his canopied bed his barons and knights murmured together in polyglot French and English. The bishops prayerfully in Latin were all eyes for the crown, laid aside as too heavy for that sunken head to carry.

And how much, they asked themselves, would the next one give to them and the Church? Little enough if it were his son Richard who would spend every mark he could raise from the lords and their villeins, their serfs and the Scottish king over the border for yet another Crusade against the Infidel whom, ever since his boyhood, he had been boiling to fight, and this time — to beat the Saracen!

'Not a hope!' gloomily opined the barons, remembering the butchery and complete overthrow of the Christian armies in the two previous Crusades, notwithstanding that the knights of St John and of the Red Cross had crowned Godfrey of Bouillon first King of Jerusalem this hundred years ago, crowned him with gold in the city where the Saviour had been crowned with thorns.

The younger knights gathered at the bedside of this second Henry were laying odds, *sotto voce*, as to how long he would last.

'A day?'

'Two days.'

'A hundred to one he'll go before this nightfall, by the look of him...'

His eldest son had been sent for, and the purple-robed physicians having done with the leeches taken from that body sucked dry of what blood was left in it, pronounced him in a 'trance', although every so often he muttered unintelligibly, most of it — if understood at all — damned himself and his God for bringing him to this pass with so much yet to do.

Lying there in semi-coma, did he see, as a drowning man is supposed to see, the pageant of his life pass before him? Did he relive the long years of his reign fraught with revolt of his sons from Normandy to the Pyrenees? But he could not have foreseen that of all monarchs to wear the Crown of England since his forbear, William of Normandy had won it from Harold, the last of the Saxon kings, he would have brought such lasting and beneficial service to his country to go down in history as the 'Great Plantagenet'. And this, despite his tyrannical autocracy, his supreme megalomania, his foul-mouthed blasphemies and his ungovernable rages that caused the unjust imprisonment of his Queen Eleanor who had dared defy him and incite his sons to war against him, all save the most loved of them, his youngest and dearest, John …

Eleanor, his wife, heiress of Aquitaine, was the divorced queen of Louis VII of France. Henry, a boy of eighteen to her thirty years, had been forced into a loveless marriage with her who, so exigeant were her demands upon his youthful ardour, wonder it was he had energy enough to pursue his own desires with women 'in or out of court' as his knights gave it with sniggers, 'to run through them like a clyster!'

Henry's eager response to Eleanor's insatiable rapacity may have compensated for her frustrated sexual life with Louis, her sickly former husband whom she disparaged as 'not worth a rotten apple and less able than a monk!'

Nothing of the monk was Henry, of whom his wife's transports had begotten him eight children in as many years, though only three daughters and two sons were still alive.

Did he, as he lay there wasted, moribund, torture himself with the memory of how, indirectly, he had been the murderer of his one-time closest friend and counsellor, Thomas Becket? Yes, indirectly, since he had had no hand in that dastardly deed before the altar of Canterbury Cathedral. And how in one of his uncontrollable rages he had ordered four of his knights, 'Go! Finish him!'

Did he remember how he had hobbled barefoot to the tomb where lay the corpse of him they had 'finished', because Archbishop Becket had crowned his son Henry ('the Young King', they called him) instead of York whose business it should have been to perform that mock ceremony? Did the old king see himself barefoot, stripped of his clothes, kneeling at the tomb to present his naked back to the monks to be scourged, crying, 'Mercy, my Lord Saviour! You who were scourged for our redemption even as I am now scourged for my sins!'

Did he masochistically enjoy the memory of those thirty-six hours he passed in that death-cold vault where lay the body of the man he believed he had murdered in thought if not in deed, and suffered a sneezing cold as a result of it? Could he have known that he who had first come to him on a lame pack-mule with his baggage on his saddle and himself in rags would be raised from his beggary to sit at the king's table, break bread with him and end up as Archbishop of Canterbury, to go down to posterity as St Thomas the Martyr? Poor comfort to him if he *had* known of it who in one of his demoniacal furies had caused his martyrdom.

And as he recalled the passage of years, half in and half out of his senses, did he see the face of the one love of his life, Rosamond Clifford? 'Fair Rosamond' they called her for her loveliness, she who had borne him two sons: one Geoffrey,

Bishop of Lincoln subsequently elevated to York, the other William Longsword, so named for the length of his weapon that sliced off men's heads in battle as he would slice off the head of a pig. Did he believe the tales that were floated concerning Rosamond's death in the convent where she betook herself as penance for bedding with the king? It was told among the courtiers that this Rosamond Clifford had been poisoned when she lay sick of a fever. Yes, poisoned by the king's queen, Eleanor, who brought her a bowl of broth for her comfort. Out of jealousy, as talk would have it; yet if jealous of this one why did she not kill off the rest of them? That Rosamond had given him those two bastard boys, more loyal than his lawful sons who were continually at war with him, was as certain that Eleanor incited their sons to fight against him, for which — and for her indiscriminate adultery — he gaoled her.

But as he lay in his semi-coma his prayers were unlikely to have been for his wife. His most conscious thought was to know who were his enemies, other than his son Richard, regrettably his heir. He had earned his father's hatred not only because he had deserted him and allied himself to Philip Augustus of France on such intimate terms that they shared the same meals and, as was said, the same bed. Henry uneasily 'marvelled as to what this might mean'...

The last of the sun thrust a dying shaft of gold through the narrow window and hovered about that head where the grey hair receded from its balding forehead, on which time had traced its lines of strife and tribulation.

As the procession of his fading life passed before him, did he again encounter young Philip of France who demanded that Richard should marry his sister Alais, intended for the king's eldest son Henry? Another renegade dead, not in honest battle but of dysentery, or more likely the pox, unmourned by his father as a good riddance.

This marriage of Richard with Philip's sister would, as Henry saw it, bring an end to the everlasting snatch-and-grab from the French king (that whining booby always sickening of some imaginary illness and lechering after his pages and his knights' young esquires and Henry's son Richard). But he, as usual, opposed anything his father wished of him, backed up by that old vixen, his high-handed dominant queen — the devil was in her, not a doubt of it, fretted the king. *She* had made Richard what he is, spoiled him, his mother's darling from his birth.

'So what now?' He raised himself from the pillows; temporarily recovered, to the surprised dismay of his physicians. What if they had made a false diagnosis and he was not to die — yet? The leeches might have performed their function and restored him to health...

The bishops and priests, eyes heavenward, thanked God that at least they might still enjoy his bounty, not much of it in his best of health, yet more than Richard would dole out to them. *He* cared for nothing but war...

'Hey ... you all! What now!' the weak voice, gaining strength, hailed them. 'I wish the treaty read ... the names of those that fought against me, ravaged my lands and allied themselves to Philip ... traitors, God damn them! Who are they? *Read!*'

This treaty should have been read a week ago when the kings of England and France had met on the plain of Colombières to discuss it, but, according to Roger de Hovenden — one of the contemporary chroniclers who today are the gossip writers of the press, and equally unreliable — a sudden storm had sprung up with a terrific clap of thunder that sent the two kings rushing for safety to their tents. Henry, drenched to the skin, rode back to his castle of Chinon, was put to bed with a warming-pan, and in that bed he now lay with a fever in his lungs, but...

'Now! What now?' he again demanded. 'The treaty ... read it. *Read!*'

More strength was in that voice with colour deepened in the fever-flushed cheeks. The knights who were laying wagers on his immediate death began to raise their odds. 'Two hundred to one he'll last for a week!'

The king's bastard son Geoffrey, Chancellor and Bishop of Lincoln, who had hastened to fetch the treaty from where in his keeping it had been placed, now returned. Henry, between gurgling coughs, spitting of mucus, and a steaming bowl of a vaporous concoction under his nose to ease his chest, repeated his demand: 'Read! Read!'

And Geoffrey, unfolding the document, read the first name on the list: that of his son John!

'No!' The denial was harshly croaked. 'No — not John! My dearest beloved — the only faithful — not he, you lie! It is Richard who betrays me —' Then, awfully, in a voice that cracked on a high despairing note, he damned to hell 'this disciple of Satan, my son ... John! May he burn in eternal ... hell fire!'

In vain did the shocked clerics implore him to retract his words and ask forgiveness of God for those curses in his hour of death. He would not retract one word of them.

'I curse my son John ... to hell!'

The king fell back against his pillows. The red flush faded from his cheeks, his jaw dropped, a hideous sound rattled in his throat as all breath left the body of Henricus Secundus Plantagenet.

'Wish I'd kept to my hundred to one before nightfall!' grumbled the knight who had lost his bet.

No sooner was the news of his father's serious illness brought to Richard at Tours than he set off at high speed for the long journey to Chinon. He was attended by Bertran de Born, his confidential gossip and troubadour, who delighted him with his erotic and satirical verses set to music by Richard or his minstrel boy, Blondel. And besides Bertran de Born was a newcomer, Ambroise — part poet, part troubadour, wholly arch-gossip — whose eyewitness accounts of the King Crusader in or out of court have been preserved throughout the ages.

A courtier had been sent in advance to find suitable lodgings for the Count of Anjou, Duke of Aquitaine and his suite. After several halts along the way the duke was housed in a reasonably good hostel, and if his bed were bug-ridden, he had endured worse. When he arrived at the village of Chinon, huddled at the foot of the castle, he told his retinue, 'Bide awhile,' handed the reins of his horse to a servant, and made off up the narrow street past filthy hovels where the serfs were housed and a row of cottages inhabited by villeins of the lords. He picked his way through the refuse flung from windows where scavenger dogs rooted in the gutters among human excrement and muck to find the maggoty carcass of a cat or a fish head. With a sniff of disgust, the fastidious Richard turned aside from a mess of pig's dung and the snarling yap of a dog whose feast he had interrupted, and turned into a more salubrious lane where stood a house in a walled garden. Pushing open a wicket gate, he walked up a path between a flourish of weeds to a door, where stood a woman. With arms outstretched in welcome, her voice dwindled to a murmur of his name.

'So long is it since you went away, I hardly dared hope you would get my message when I heard you had been sent for to the king.'

'What is it,' he asked brusquely, 'that you want of me which is so urgent?'

'They talk of your marriage to the Princess of France, and I was anxious to know if 'tis true.'

'What is it to you if it be true or false?' He glowered down at her from his great height and massive frame that dwarfed hers.

'It is everything to me,' she flared, her face flushed with a rise of colour to her suntanned cheeks. A brown-eyed girl, dark-haired, full-bosomed, full-lipped, she returned him a scowl, saying, 'Come in and I'll show you what it is to me that you take a wife — you who have sworn you had no use for marriage. Come in!'

'I will not,' he said turning from her, 'come in to your' (sarcastically) 'castle. I am behind time already for attendance on the king.'

'But —' she showed her fine teeth in what was less of a smile than a threatening grin — 'I have something to show you as a memento of your visit to me these ten months since.'

At that moment, from a room into which the door opened, came a whimpering cry that rose to a demanding crescendo.

With a look of amazed apprehension Richard pushed her aside and entered the room. The furniture of the houseplace, as the one living room of the cottage was called, led to a kitchen. This contained a trestle table, some two or three stools, a stink of decaying food, and a screaming infant in a cot.

'Behold your son!'

With another of those grins at Richard, the woman lifted the baby in her arms and gave him her breast. At once the yells were silenced. Greedily he sucked, subsided, and slept.

'This is none of mine!' Richard swung round furiously to tell her. 'There was no chance of you begetting it from me — as well you know!'

'What I well know,' she retorted, clutching the infant closer, 'and before God and the Holy Cross I swear it — that no other than you has ever had of me!'

He caught her roughly by the shoulders. 'You lying bitch. How comes it then that I found you broken?'

'How could you have found me broken if you had not pierced me? 'Tis *you* who lie!'

'I had none of you,' he told her fiercely. 'You enticed me to raise me a horn, and that's all you got from me. So take your brat to the man who begot it, for I did not!'

'Who else but you, Richard?' She backed from him, rubbing her shoulder. 'Don't. You are too strong — you've bruised me. You know that no man but you has ever —' she spat at him the old Saxon word in common use then as now — 'with me.'

'I know *this*. That you know I am my father's heir since my brother Henry — God damn his soul — got himself crowned and fought against me with the Poitevin Barons to take Aquitaine. But he died before he could get what he wanted. And now my father is like to die you saddle me with a king's bastard. Yes! You know well enough how my father's two by-blows did benefit with Rosamond, their mother. But you'll get no benefit from me, my girl, for what is not and never could be mine!'

With that he turned to go, but she caught at his sleeve. 'Why do you come to me now, then? Did you learn from your gossip de Born that I was going to show myself to you and to your father with his grandson — to shame you?'

'I have heard nothing from de Born or from anyone else of you or any other woman.'

'Hah-ah!' She threw back her head, her wide mouth opening to a hoarse laugh to show her large white teeth and her uvula.

'You have the teeth of a shark,' he told her disgustedly.

'So have I, but you have felt them, my lord, in your stiffest parts when you enjoyed me in the way a man enjoys a woman. Yet I can well believe what is flown all over Anjou, that your tastes run to the Bulgars — they who follow the doctrine of the Cathars that swear love between man and woman is love of the devil, and that marriage between *them* is the sin of sodomy. So they name you Richard the Bulgar. But you can refute it, for here —' she held the child up to him — 'is evidence of your potency with me if not with any other woman.'

'Dare say these calumnies,' he blazed, 'and I'll call my men to have you hanged for treason!'

'Have a care, Richard, how you sling *your* calumnies at me, for you cast treason at the son of a king, as he will be in this next hour or two.'

Without deigning to throw another look at her he stormed from the room, ignoring the name she called after him: 'Richard! That is how the priest baptised him a week ago. Richard Fitzrichard of Chinon!'

He returned to his waiting retinue to be greeted by de Born. 'What kept you? Or can I guess?'

'Guess what you like, and I'll thank you not to spew gossip from your big mouth to spray me with any man's whore. Get on, now. I am too delayed thanks to your mischievous babble!'

So on they went, Richard heading the cavalcade, caring nothing for the children who gambolled in the cobbled street and scattered barely in time to escape his horse's hooves.

Arriving at the castle of Chinon, where a major-domo obsequiously received him, he marched on to his father's bedchamber, travel-stained and dusty as he was from a three-day journey. At the door he paused. The chanting of kneeling priests and the bowed heads of those who stood beside the bed told him what lay beneath that covered form.

He made a swift movement to drag aside the heavy canopy that half concealed the body, and pulled the coverlet from the face of death. Then an exclamation of horror broke from him, for he saw that trickles of blood oozed from each nostril, and there came to him the memory of an old wives' tale told him by the woman who had suckled him, his nurse Hodierna. (She must have been the only wet nurse in history who has had a village named after her: Knoyle Hodierna in Wiltshire.)

Watching that ooze of blood, he recalled how his old nurse had said a corpse would bleed in the presence of its murderer. With a strangled cry Richard fell on his knees beside the dead, and prayed aloud in agony, 'Lord God forgive me if my sin has caused the death of my father! I have warred against him, and now in death he accuses me...'

Those who heard him, not too engrossed with their spiritual duties, exchanged glances. The younger knights hid grins behind their praying hands, the barons feigned deafness, for Richard's outburst had no disquieting effect upon them. They all knew he had warred against and defied his father in his command to marry the Princess of France. (And not without reason, they agreed between themselves, knowing — as did his son — that Alais of France had succeeded Rosamond as the late king's mistress.) There were many who looked forward to the new reign, and a more likeable monarch than his unpredictable and violent-tempered predecessor.

Yet Richard had more to disturb him than Hodierna's grisly tale of a corpse's accusation of murder. The king had desired he should be buried in the Abbey of Fontevrault, and Richard had to see that his father's last wish be carried out. He ordered William the Marshal, and his half-brother Geoffrey, late Bishop of Lincoln, to have the body brought to the abbey, which was within walking distance of the castle.

There Henry lay in state before the high altar, surrounded by kneeling priests and nuns praying for the soul of the departed. The watch extended through the third night when the abbey was emptied, not without some thanksgiving on the part of the prayerful, for although the month was July it had rained prodigiously and the chapel where the king lay was damp and cold. But the next day when Richard came again to see the body of his father, he was met with a commotion headed by William the Marshal. This was the first time they had exchanged more than a word or two since they had met in battle during one of the many revolts of the king's sons against their father and the monarchy. Robbers, he was told by a grim Lord Marshal, had entered the abbey the night before, and scarcely a ring had been found on the king's fingers, not a crown for his head, no sceptre for his hand, and only trumpery makeshifts to replace them.

Beckoning the Marshal to speak aside with him, Richard faced the man who had unhorsed him at the Battle of Le Mans. To have brought down Richard was a mighty victory for William the Marshal, who was about half his size and had nothing of his strength. Those who watched wondered if the Duc d'Aquitaine, as yet uncrowned their king, would have his revenge here before the carcass of his father!

But once out of hearing Richard turned to the man, who stood there in some apprehension, unarmed as he was. He need not have feared, for softly spoken at that moment was Richard. 'Sir Marshal, had I received your spear thrust it would have been the end of me.'

'My lord,' replied the Marshal, 'I slew only your horse, and of that I do repent. I offer myself now for Your Highness's revenge.'

At which Richard slapped a heavy hand upon the shrinking shoulder of the Marshal. 'All is forgiven. Your loyalty to my father, God rest his soul, is not by me forgotten.' He knew he must cultivate the friendship of all who had been his father's adherents to ensure that he could leave his kingdom of England to those who would deputise, more or less faithfully, for him.

His younger brother John hastened to join Richard so soon as he had learned of their father's death. And he fervently hoped, since he knew Richard was bent on pursuing a third Crusade, that he would never return, since so many others before him lay rotting in the sandy desert, a feast for vultures.

John already held Nottinghamshire, Derbyshire and Dorset, granted to him by his doting father, besides a long chain of castles. And now, when Richard had made his peace with William the Marshal, he found John at his side, full of grief and tears.

'This is so sorry a bereavement,' John sobbed, while he inly prayed that in the not-far-distant future he would see himself King of England, Duke of Aquitaine, Count of Anjou. Although it was known that Richard had been betrothed to Alais, daughter of the late King of France and sister to the present King Philip, he also knew that his brother had no intention of marrying the Princess Alais, that he had repeatedly defied his father's earnest wish, and that it was unlikely Richard would marry any woman. As to begetting him an heir if he were persuaded to marry, John knew, or had learned from his toadies, that Richard was not named 'the Bulgar' for nothing!

But the face upturned to his brother showed no expression more than sorrow for the death of the father whose favourite son he knew himself to be; nor had he heard, as yet, how he had been cursed to hell with his father's dying breath...

'John Lackland,' so called for the small slices of England assigned to him, was the antithesis of his brother: slight of build where Richard was broad, short where Richard was tall, pale of face while Richard was ruddy, his hair and beard tow-coloured while Richard's were a flame of red-shot gold. John's eyes were narrow and Richard's crystal-clear blue. He had ever been envious of his brother's magnificent physique; nor did he share Richard's love of music and his 'cranky versifying', as he contemptuously regarded the poems his brother wrote. Only one or two of these have been preserved. Richard's determination to arm himself and his Crusaders for another war against the Saracens — that lunatic project, as John saw it — was all to the good since it might well bring about his ascendance to the throne in the not-far-distant future, for which he never ceased to pray.

John contentedly nurtured news of the appalling conditions prevalent among the armies that had already succumbed to the deadly toll of pestilence which ravaged the Holy Land, and the massacre of Knight Templars captured by the Infidel in the two earlier Crusades. Why should Richard, despite his splendid health and strength, be spared where so many were not? One could but hope.

Yet only heartbroken grief and loyalty was in the warm embrace with which his arms enfolded the king.

'Dearest brother! While I grieve for and with you in this most bitter loss, I rejoice that our beloved country and your kingdom will henceforth be ruled with wisdom and piety, God be praised!'

Disengaging, Richard rubbed a finger on his cheek where John had left a clammy kiss, and told him with a grin, 'You know you are only waiting to have me out and yourself in.' Then, to lessen the sting of that, he amended it by telling him with a laugh and a pat on John's shoulder so heavy that it caused him to stagger, 'But while I am in possession you shan't "lack land" of all that may be yours one day. I'll give you the counties of Devon, Somerset and Cornwall, where you may sit biting your nails till I and my Kingdom Come be gone!'

Backing from another embrace while John forced more tears from his watery eyes to blubber effusive thanks. 'You are too generous for one so unworthy as I, dearest brother, and —'

Richard cut him short by seizing John's hand to say, 'I see you still bite your nails — down to the quick! A dirty habit for which our nurse Hodierna used to put mustard on them to cure you, which it didn't, and never will until you get what you want, and that may not be all you hope for. Kingship is a full-time and thankless job, and brings with it more thraldom than that of the meanest serf, unless he has a dagger up his sleeve to strike his masters!'

'Dear brother,' tearfully said John, 'you will always have your little jest at my expense, as in our nursery days.'

'Not *our* nursery days,' was the cool reply. '*Your* nursery days, when I, at sixteen, was warring with the Gauls and my father alongside our brother Henry, who should be where I am now had he not sickened of the pox or bloody flux. It wasn't. It was from eating a bad oyster out of season. His greed for what he fancied would ever outweigh his reason even to his choice of a wife, Margaret, daughter of Louis of France by his second wife after his divorce from our mother, which smacks somewhat of incest. It looks like to run in the family, which is why I defied our father. He would have me marry Alais of France, who was one of our godly father's women, and he seduced her while in waiting on our mother. But of course you knew that.'

'N-no, I did not,' John, who did know that, said with simulated shock.

Richard continued, 'As for those western shires of England, you are welcome to them and the whole of my island of fog that is still a haven for barbarians, yet unrecovered from the invasion of our forbear of Normandy, whose redheaded son Rufus laid waste to all his father had won for us, and got an arrow in his arse for his sins while out hunting with one of his knights. Whether that knight, Sir Walter Tyrell, shot him or mis-aimed at a stag, as he swore was the case, is not known, but it had to be accepted as an accident that none then or now believes. So you see, 'tis no great advantage to be a king. For me, I'll take up the Cross so soon as my crowning is over, for I'd liefer you sat to be anointed in Westminster than I. Don't bother to say me "Nay", Richard told him with a grin. They call me Richard "Yea and Nay", so I'll be "Yea" for you, as I'm always of two minds.

John returned him a sickly smile, not at all caring for the remainder of Richard's two minds 'Yea and Nay', that might decide against his offer of those counties in the king's 'island of fog'.

Having put his affairs of Aquitaine, Anjou and Touraine in order, Richard returned to Normandy. At Rouen he was girded with the Ducal sword and invested with the Duchy of Normandy, and at Rouen he held his first court as King Elect of England, to be warmly congratulated by John with more fervent embraces.

From Rouen, with John trotting beside him, and behind him all those he presumed to be faithful, but trusting none who swore fidelity other than his young troubadour Blondel and — with reservations — Bertran de Born, Richard came to Barfleur and sailed for Southampton.

As for John, Richard kept a wary eye on him but made no attempt to deny him the right to stand by while the king's treasurer weighed and counted their father's monetary assets, worth almost a quarter of a million marks. This was done to the satisfaction of John, who calculated that in God's good time the late king's fortune, with the whole of the English and Norman domains, would be his.

So soon as the king's death had been announced, Queen Eleanor, who had been released from prison by her husband after eleven years of captivity, at once made a triumphant tour throughout her son's English kingdom. In his name she released and pardoned all prisoners so that Richard's accession to his throne would assure his subjects of his clemency as opposed to the late king's intolerance.

All this was excellent; but the more prudent of the Queen Mother's advisers — as reported by William of Newburgh, a chronicler of the time — suggested that such clemency in the name of King Richard, on behalf of the prisoners awaiting their trials and the hideous punishment of blinding and castration, could bring about some violent disturbance.

Among the many transgressors set at liberty to pursue their thieving, poaching, or minor as well as major iniquities, was one Robin Hood. Not that he had yet been condemned. He was awaiting trial for robbing the rich to give to the poor, and with his band of followers he had assumed lawless dominion in Sherwood Forest. It was said that the new king, while still Count of Anjou, had been apprised of such a one. It is likely that Richard recognised in the tales told of this romantic adventurer a man after his own heart, a crusader to break and remake the Forest laws, offering justice to the needy, depriving their bloated barons of their fatted calves to feed the starving serfs.

After the king and his brother John landed at Southampton they were met by the Queen Mother at Winchester. There was universal rejoicing at the reunion of mother and son after Eleanor's long imprisonment. John also came in for his share of attention, especially from the women of the town, who saw in the puny, pale, fair-haired prince a neglected younger son overshadowed by his handsome elder brother.

'The poor lad,' whispered the market women who had gathered to watch the coming of Richard, 'so neglected and unwanted by the queen who has eyes for naught but the king.'

''Tis said that this King Richard,' went the murmur behind hands, 'is not King Henry's son. She was divorced by her first husband, the King of France.'

'And sought after and courted by others, kings or nothing!' went the rumour that fell on John's ears, ever on the alert to gather what gleanings he could, even to the supposed bastardy of Richard, to further his hopes of kingship; for there was no knowing to what danger his brother's mad fanatical crusading might lead him ... or end him!

However, sufficient for the day while John bided his time, to all intent the devoted brother joining in the general rejoicing as he accompanied the king on his leisurely progress through the kingdom of which he knew little, having lived almost all his life in Normandy and Aquitaine when not at war.

At Marlborough John, who had been officially betrothed to Isabella, daughter of the Earl of Gloucester, was married in haste and unwillingly to her, as he had an eye on Princess Alais of France, destined to be the wife of Richard — a more fitting consort, he had decided, for a future King John than the daughter of an earl, even if heiress of Gloucester. None the less, and with inward hate and outward love, John was duly wedded to the plain and dumpy Isabella, with the thought that he could easily dispose of her were he to take the Princess of France for his queen.

So soon as the nuptials in the Earl of Gloucester's castle were over, the bride and bridegroom attended the king and his entourage to Windsor where they rejoined the Queen Mother; and so to London.

This was Richard's first sight of his capital, since he had never gone farther in England than Winchester, on two short visits when a boy. A heartening sight it was for him to see, as he entered the city, the narrow beflagged streets thronged with his subjects roaring themselves hoarse in welcome to their Sovereign Lord.

Riding at the head of his cavalcade Richard would have seen, in this Plantagenet London, a city of churches. From the great cathedrals to the smallest parish church, from stately monasteries and the colleges of priests, he would have heard the sonorous clash and music of church bells ring out to drown the cacophonous clamour of apprentices crying their wares at their stalls. And for miles beyond the city could be heard the music of the bells in the pastures of Hampstead or the green slopes of Highgate, where a hundred years later one Richard Whittington would set out to seek his fortune and would be summoned back to London, so legend has it, by those very bells that welcomed King Richard of England to his capital.

It was a happier world concentrated in this first King Richard's London, where men followed each to himself his skilled labour: the goldsmiths in Old Change, the ironmongers in Ironmonger Lane; the butchers in St Nicholas Shambles and the Stock Market, where live cattle were sold; the hosiers in Hosier Lane and the paternoster sellers in Paternoster Row.

Within London's walls the citizens made everything Londoners required and brought to be sold by journeymen, wagoners, carters to all parts of the country; wines, spices, cloths, silks, velvets, and wimples for women; helmets, pikes, swords, spears and bows for the crossbowmen, were made by the makers of such. Every kind of trade was carried on within the city: mills for grinding corn, breweries for brewing beer; the melting of tallow for candles, lard and glue, offering their malodorous products in the aptly named Stinking Lane. And the roar and the racket of the narrow streets leading down to the Thames could be heard so far as the Surrey Hills. None was disturbed by the ear-splitting, ceaseless confusion of noise, the yelling and shouting and cheering that greeted the king on his way to Westminster. And above all this, to deafen him who in peaceful Anjou had never heard the like of it — nor ever smelled the stink of it — day in and day out rang the bells.

A rip-roaring multitude welcomed the king. He, who spoke little English, stood in the stirrups bare-headed to shout in as much of their tongue as he could muster. 'God bless you, *mes amis* ... *mes* fren's, I t'ank you, *grammercie!*' He bowed low from the saddle, waving a gauntleted hand, eyes up to the windows where women's heads peeped, eyes down to the boys who ran at his stirrups to snatch at the showers of blossoms flung at the king, their fallen petals caught in the red-burnished gold of his hair to get him more yells of delight...

So, on 1 September in that year, 1189, into the City of London he rode to Westminster, to be crowned and anointed *Ricardus Rex* — known less as 'The King' than as Richard, the Heart of a Lion.

His coronation was followed by a banquet in the Palace of Westminster. The barons, knights and laity sat at separate tables. The king's mother and brother John were also seated apart, but the clergy, from the archbishops down to the lesser parish priests, were given place of honour near the king, whose deep devotion to the cause of Christ was to be his sole concern and purpose. As for women — marriage? Nothing of that for Richard who had taken the Cross and intended to embark upon a third Crusade; and if as much for the spirit of adventure as from apostolic fervour, none questioned his motive but all approved and were glad of a truly Christian king — at last.

The celebrations went on all night, with feasting and drinking and music from his minstrels in the gallery, and a choir of boys singing the *Te Deum* in praise of God and the king, who had dined and wined with the best of them and could carry better his drink than most. Certainly more than Prince John, who, his face slowly turning to a greenish pallor, was lugged from the table by a page barely in time to save him from a shaming over-spill. Then, when dawn's rosy fingers probed the apertures of windows, and some of the younger nobles and knights had each took a lady to partner at the beaming encouragement of the king — who partnered no lady — came a noisy interruption.

While the feasting and jollification continued inside the palace, outside a riot developed. Some of the wealthiest Jews of the City, much in favour with the late king (for munificent loans at a low rate of interest to imburse the exchequer) had come to the palace with gifts for the king's coronation.

While the king sat at meat, as a contemporary chronicler gives it, *the rabbish* (presumably 'rabble') *upped and with staves, bats, and stones laid about the unbelieving Jews to make them flee...*

Worse was to follow.

Those who escaped a beating-up fled to their ghettoes only to find their synagogues ravaged, their houses ransacked and in flames, their money and valuables stolen. Their families, caught in the fires, were done to death, men, women and children shrieking in their agony, devoured by the flames while stray dogs prowled among the cindered flesh and bones.

When news of this appalling pogrom came to Richard he 'waxed exceeding wroth', as was said, and sent some of his knights and barons to investigate and punish those responsible for this outrage 'to his innocent people'.

'Innocent?' cried the horrified clergy. 'How innocent are they who denied and crucified our Lord Jesus?' And he consigned them to hell to be burnt in everlasting. As did those of London's citizens who loathed the sight of the browngaberdined, despised race of 'blood-sucking vermin', so described by another who had witnessed this monstrous persecution.

But the king's tolerance of the 'blood-sucking vermin' served him little, since the damage to their property and the theft of gold from their coffers depleted much of the promised assistance that the wealthiest of 'vermin' had gratefully offered the king for his mercy, and to further his quest of the Cross.

'A sorry end,' deplored Richard, 'is this to the joy of my crowning...' But a less sorry end with his mother, if of more consequence, followed those three festive days.

TWO

The indomitable Eleanor, now in her sixties, retained much of the beauty that had enslaved the kings of France, England and others, not of such high estate. She bore down upon her son in his apartment where he sat in conference with William Longchamp, whom Richard had created Bishop of Ely, and who was well in the running for the chancellorship in exchange for three thousand pounds to finance the king's Crusade.

'The king,' remarked Richard of Devizes, 'would unburden any whose money did not burden them. He showed himself as able at drawing from possible or impossible sources as were any of his Jewish friends.'

When the Queen Mother gained admittance to the king, who had expressly ordered he should not be disturbed while in conference, she whose hard grey steely eye would rouse the fear of God in anyone — even her son Richard — swept aside the French knight, William de Barres, who stood guarding the door.

'What?' exclaimed Eleanor. Her eyes, sharp as knives, raked de Barres from his blond head to his long pointed shoes. 'Do you dare detain me? Get away!' The ample sleeve of her gown as she swept an arm across him caught at the jewelled clasp of his cloak to loosen a stone that fell to the ground. Ignoring the mishap and de Barres, now grovelling at her feet to retrieve the ruby fallen from the clasp, the incensed Queen Mother pushed by him into the hall. This, as in all mansions and castles of the Great, contained recesses that opened from the main hall and were used either as bedchambers or retiring rooms by the members of the court. One of the largest of these was used by the king while in residence at the palace in order to conduct affairs of state.

Like a ship in full sail, her long wide sleeves and the veil attached to her conical headdress floating in the breeze from the window guiltless of glass, the dowager queen descended on her son and his Bishop Longchamp. A hideous little monkey of a man was he, who sprang to his feet and bowed nose to knees at the entrance of the queen; while Richard, also rising if with less humility and a flush of embarrassment, asked, 'To what, Madam, am I beholden for this, er, this welcome visit?'

'Welcome or unwelcome,' was the reply in imperative emphasis, 'I am here, and here I stay, that I may speak with you — alone.' Pointing to the chair Longchamp had vacated, 'Leave us,' she commanded, 'and — go!' With a nod from Richard, Longchamp was dismissed.

'Draw that curtain.' Eleanor indicated one of purple leather that hung at the window's aperture. 'What I have to say is for your ear alone and not for your little ape of a Longchamp or any other of your toadies, especially your pernickety carpet-knight de Barres: I'd make a clean sweep of the lot o' them had I my way, which should be *your* way were you not so besottedly indulgent to them who pander to your versifying and the tira-lira of your harp and lyre when you are not driving any from here to the border of Scotland to come to your call of the Cross.' And, seating herself, she waved her son also to sit, for he stood as he was used to do in her or his father's presence until bidden to be seated. He was not yet accustomed to taking precedence before 'Her Almightiness', as he privately named his formidable mother.

'What were you discussing so close, heads together, with your Longchamp?' she demanded.

'I have to appoint one whom I can trust to take over my — that is to say —' he floundered, feeling as always totally inadequate when discussing his monarchical duties with her, the only woman he had ever loved, who had ruled him since his birth — 'that is, I must have one whom I can trust to — to deputise for me when I am in the Holy Land.'

The lady reared her head. 'To make him — this Longchamp, your Governor — a regent in your absence? Good God!'

'Better he than John, who is scarcely able enough and experienced enough as yet to undertake what would amount to — to a regency,' Richard made bold to suggest.

'Tchah!' or some such sound issued from the queen as she brushed aside the veil from her headgear, which the breeze had blown over her face. 'Pull the curtain,' she ordered. 'I cannot stand this draught.' He rose to obey and, the curtain drawn, the recess was plunged in gloom.

'Ring for lights,' was the Queen Mother's next command; and as Richard tinkled a hand bell on the table, 'When,' she wished to know, 'will these benighted English learn how to do as we in Aquitaine and Normandy have done for years, with glass to our windows brought from Venice?' She shuddered. 'I would perish of the damp and cold should I be forced to live in this fog-begotten island.' And to the page who had answered the bell, 'Bring candles.' These were brought and lighted; when the page withdrew, 'I have this,' she said, 'to tell you.'

And she told: 'With me in your palace is Alais of France — yes, you may stare! I sent for her to be here for your crowning, that you take her to wed before you embark on your crazy crusade. You must get you an heir, the marriage must be consummated now — you understand? For should you —

God forbid — never return from the Holy Land, which is more than likely what with pestilence and Saladin's barbarous tortures and captures and merciless massacres, you'll have none to follow you save Geoffrey's two-year-old son Arthur or — John. And what sort of a king would *he* make? As much use as the toddler, of whom he'd be quick enough to dispose, if I know my son John. And how I ever begot such a one only the devil can know. So,' she leaned forward to lay a hand on the fist he had clenched on the table between them, 'will you see Alais? She is willing and ready enough, as is her brother, to keep to your father's pledge that you wed Philip's sister Alais. You cannot afford to fall out with Philip, who is crazy mad as yourself to take up the Cross and be murdered by Saladin's infidels.'

'If I see her,' Richard offered hesitant compromise, 'I do not commit myself to — marry her?'

'To be sure,' his mother winningly agreed, 'the choice of a bride rests with you, naturally.'

'Yes, naturally,' he dared to take her up on that, 'and not unnaturally. You know, as do I, that my father seduced her and took her to bed as like a dozen others!'

'More's the pity,' snapped his mother, 'you didn't have at least half as many as your father enjoyed, to make the world disbelieve in your liking for men rather than women, for all you have begotten a son — so they say.'

'So *she* says, for my sins,' he blurted, 'and that a wanton should have at me who was too full of liquor to know! But I swear —' he thumped a fist on the table — 'by God's blood I swear it — I never begot her with issue, for on my oath I never coupled with a woman in my life!'

'Time then that you did!' retorted his mother. 'For a man of your age to declare yourself virgin is a slur on your manhood.'

'Or a credit to my sense. That bitch, hoping to hand me a bastard, only thought of it when 'twas certain my father was dying so to give me another man's brat with a royal bar sinister! Can you wonder if I despise women, unless —' his face lightened in a grin that regressed him to the boy Richard of twelve, rather than the man of two and thirty — 'unless,' he repeated, 'she were of the Amazons incarnate from the Greeks to go with me in armour to fight for the Cross, or were she to partake in a tourney sooner than throw down the gauntlet in safety above!'

'Better she go forth with you armoured in naught but her shift,' said the mother to his engaging grin that never failed to weaken her. 'Will you then see her?' she coaxed.

'Oh … so be it! But I'll promise her nothing — nor you, Mother, nor brother Philip — do you hear me?'

'That's my good boy.' She got up to pat his shoulder and receive his warm kiss. 'And you will — you positively *must* — take you a wife, be she Amazon, armoured or not, so to beget you an heir.' She moved to pull aside the leathern curtain at the entrance. 'Or else, mark me well, your England — God help us — will have a King John.'

Long after she left him he sat at the table, his quill scribbling an indeterminate pattern on an empty parchment until, unconsciously, a girl's face appeared in the hieroglyphics as his thoughts swung back some three or four years to a tourney at Navarre when on a visit to her father King Sancho VI. How was she called? An outlandish name, Berria-something, sister of his friend Sancho, a great one for jousting and much older than she.

A dark-haired, dark-eyed sprig of a girl, not more than twelve or thirteen years, with large wide-apart eyes and lashes so long you could hang rings on 'em. He recalled how she was dressed in a sleeveless tunic to her ankles, worn over an undergarment fitting closely to the flat small breasts — the customary dress for a girl not yet past her childhood — and her hair cut short as a page's. She had sat between Richard and her father, the King of Navarre, those eyes, dark-lashed, fixed on the two knights riding into the lists to engage in the tourney.

She turned excitedly to her father. 'See! I am to judge these two — the black knight, Philippe, my cousin, is my choice, he did overthrow my brother, Sancho, last tourney — he is the one who will win!'

'Not to be so sure,' her father bade her, and lowered an eyelid over her head to Richard. 'She would enter the lists herself,' he chuckled, 'were she the son her mother — God rest her — prayed for and died of a daughter, least wanted. She was ever more of a boy than a girl.' His tone, and the down-glancing look he bestowed on his daughter, confirmed her as the apple of his eye.

In the galleries the harsh bright colours of the women's gowns resembled nothing so much, Richard remembered, as a border of variegated flowers in direct contrast to the sober brown tunic and cream-coloured dress of the little princess at his side. She was jumping up and down in her excitement, cheering in shrill treble the knight she favoured and who looked to be the better of the two.

'Have at him!' She waved her hand, stripped of its glove and flung into the arena, as she shouted, 'You'll be the winner!' Her voice was drowned in the clash of steel and the thud of horses' hooves amid the dust kicked up from the sand. 'Oh! You —

Philippe!' she yelled, and turned excitedly to Richard. 'I am to give the prize to the winner — he is my cousin.'

But she did not give the prize to the son of Count Philip of Flanders, for he was the loser of the fray, unhorsed by the knight, his contestant.

A whimsical smile came upon Richard's lips as his pen re-dipped, darkened the cropped hair framing a childish face. He recalled her flame of anger when she saw her knight vanquished, and how her father soothed her, saying, 'Come, my dear, 'tis not a fight, only a friendly joust so to use themselves well in battle.'

'I do not care if 'tis friendly or not — for me it is a fight,' she told him, sulky-mouthed, 'but I'll give my cousin of Flanders my trophy just the same. He should have won as he'd win in a battle, he knows *all* of battle and war.'

'Well, well!' Richard shrugged away that glimpse of her he thought never to see for some few years to come, when she was still more a child than woman and less of a girl than a boy.

His coronation over, Richard lost no time in preparing for his Crusade. This haste for his departure — the raising of funds, the assemblage of ships from all seaports in England, Normandy, Poitou and Aquitaine — delayed the meeting with Princess Alais arranged by his mother.

From his Palace of Westminster the king ordered a formidable fleet of about a hundred vessels manned with eight thousand men, and besides the crews there were forty men-at-arms with their horses and the same number of foot soldiers. There were, besides, about fourteen cargo ships laden with gold, silver and jewels for bribes and — of equal importance — ample provisions for the voyage: sides of bacon, various meats, cheeses, flour, biscuits and wine galore. Richard made certain that none of his army would go short of their creature comforts. He did, however, lay down strict regulations that stern discipline must be enforced. He decreed that any man who should slay another on board would be thrown into the sea lashed to the corpse of the dead. Among other disciplinary methods, if one was found guilty of attacking a fellow shipmate to draw blood, his hand should be struck off; and if a man were found thieving he would have flung at him a bucket of pitch and the contents of a pillow shaken over him. Thus tarred and feathered, he would be an object of ridicule to his fellows.

Richard had judiciously chosen a tough lot for his armies, and his choice did not fail him; not only were they tough, but keen as he on his pilgrimage to vanquish all anti-Christs.

In December 1189 Richard sailed from Dover. As he stood on deck watching the white cliffs recede, he may have wondered how long, if ever, it would be before he saw England again.

He was to meet Philip of France at Vézelay, in April 1190 to join forces on their Crusade. They also intended to meet there the Emperor of Germany, Frederick Barbarossa, but he had started out on his Crusade six months before either of the kings of France and England, and by the time the two arrived at Vézelay, Barbarossa was dead. He had got himself drowned bathing in a river in Asia Minor after too heavy a meal.

This resulted in further delay while Richard assembled his fleet. He and Philip were then to march south through France and meet the English flotilla at Marseilles; but news was brought to Philip of the death of his wife, Queen Isabel, and this caused still further delay. Not that Philip was overwhelmed with grief as he, like Richard, cared little for women and less for his queen.

It was now almost two and a half years since Richard had taken the Cross, and it looked as if his Crusade would never be accomplished, especially after what was thought to be an ill omen. This was when he received the staff from the Archbishop of Tours and leaned on it only to break it in half, as noted by an eyewitness, Roger de Hovenden. Undismayed by that, Richard rounded on his knights, who were superstitiously muttering among themselves. 'Damn your croakings, you fools! The staff was already split.'

Then, when the two kings met at Vézelay with their joint armies, it was evident that the provisions supplied for thousands of men and horses were insufficient to carry rations across miles of desert, and that the problem could only be solved by separation of the French and English troops. It was therefore decided that the kings must each go his own way to Marseilles, there to augment their provisions as best they could.

At Marseilles on 1 August, Richard, who expected to find his fleet waiting for him, was told it had been held up in Portugal. The King of Portugal, with the promise of ample reward, had prevailed upon the English sailors to aid him in his fight against the Moors. Richard, fuming at this further setback, bought thirty ships from merchants in Marseilles and coasted toward Genoa. There he found that Philip, always hypochondriacal, had taken to his bed, lying 'sick to the stomach', he groaned to Richard, who came upon him at a house in the town.

'Well!' exclaimed Richard in disgust. 'What now? You don't look as if you're ready for the Last Sacrament.'

'I am cursed from the revolting food these Italians have fed me,' he muttered. 'It has given me the green sickness.'

'Green sickness?' exploded Richard. 'You'll have more than green sickness fed you in the Holy Land, if we ever get there. These infidels live on nothing but rice, dried oats and camel dung if they don't feed on themselves as cannibals. Get up, for God's sake if not for your own. You can't lie here with your fleet sailing ahead of you and the town full of your troops drinking themselves sodden and using any woman they can lay hands on.'

But Philip's indisposition was the least of Richard's concerns. Before he could leave Genoa, his mother who, determined he should meet his wife-to-be, had pursued her son from Westminster with Alais in tow and waylaid him as he was about to leave for Naples with the thirty ships he had bought in Marseilles.

The presentation of Alais to Richard did not augur well for the Queen Mother's hopes. Richard had not seen Alais since his boyhood, and she had then been a coltish long-legged child with nothing to recommend her to him, a lad in his teens more interested in boys than in girls. Alais had now developed into a well-formed high-nosed, arrogant young person who addressed her prospective husband with scant ceremony.

'I would have you know, Your Highness, that I have been brought to meet *votre Altesse* not of my will but at the request of *Madame* —' she indicated the queen standing beside her and offering what might have been intended as a gracious smile, but was more like a threatened cloudburst — 'of *Madame la Reine*, who is as anxious for an alliance between France and England by my marriage to yourself as I am *not!* Your Highness comprehends?'

If His Highness did comprehend, he may have been relieved at this unwelcoming reception of himself and his suit by his prospective consort, and at once responded to it. "Your Highness expresses my own sentiments regarding an alliance between ourselves and our two countries. Much as I appreciate and would be honoured,' he bowed low, 'by a union with Your Grace and my unworthy self, I am allied to your brother Philip in the Holy Pilgrimage for which, as Knights of the Cross, we have one sole aim and purpose.'

'That being so,' said Alais, entirely ignoring her intended mother-in-law, who looked as if about to explode, 'I am content to know you are as unwilling as I to be partner in a *marriage of convenience* arranged without our interest or our desire.'

For once the indomitable Eleanor was at a loss for words to disguise her mounting wrath at what she thought to be a conspiracy between these two who refused to be conveniently married. *This French girl,* she inly raged, *is no better than she ought to be — seduced by my lecher of a husband who had no use for her or any woman except in his bed. She should be thankful she has the chance of lawful bedding with another king and with a mind of her own …*

In direct contradiction to the mind of the Queen Mother — who was as anxious for this marriage as Richard was not — Alais had made it very clear that, at her convenance, she would return to France unwedded and as soon as might be. And, at her convenance, she set sail from Genoa for her native land.

'What is this I hear?' demanded Philip when, risen from his bed, he met Richard in the house he had taken for a week or two while awaiting the advice of his doctors that he was well enough to resume his journey. 'Do you refuse to keep your troth with my sister?'

'There has been no troth on her part or on mine,' he was told. 'Alais must be well aware of my personal objection to such a marriage.'

'Personal?' ejaculated Philip. 'What personal objection can you dare offer to a marriage with my sister, the Princess of France?'

'An objection as clear to her,' said Richard, 'as it is to me.'

'*Comment? Cré Bleu!*' cried Philip, with mounting indignation. 'Who could possibly know that —'

Richard cut him short. 'That your sister was my father's whore?'

'Sacred Name of a Name!' cried Philip, reddening, and clasping his long pale hands as if in prayer. 'Do you dare tell me such — such monstrous treason?'

'No, I tell you monstrous fact. My father, in his later years, endeavoured to recapture his first youthful love with the "Fair Rosamond". She should have been called the "Unfair" since she started my father's harem that began with her and ended — or we may presume it ended — with Alais. He went from the ripe to the unripe, preferring the bud to the blossom. And also —' as Philip, whose face changed from red to yellow appeared as if he relapsed to a green, or yellow, sickness — 'also it is said, if not actually confirmed, that the Princess of France supplied the late King of England with a daughter which gives me besides two half-brothers, a half-sister. So you will understand why I cannot possibly marry the woman — for woman she is now, and not the girl my father chose as his concubine — as it would savour unpleasantly of incest. Yes?'

'Ye-yes — *No! C'est incroyable!*' exclaimed the shattered Philip. 'This is the most —'

He covered his face and broke into simulated sobs that in no way affected Richard, who shook him by his narrow shoulders, saying, 'I am unimpressed by your display of emotion. You must have known what the whole of our court knew, that the child born to Alais was begot by my father.'

'You are as ever,' Philip's hands dropped to his sides, 'as hard-hearted and unfeeling as — as a codfish!'

'That a codfish has a heart which can feel nothing more than the fisherman's hook is news,' said Richard mildly, 'to me.'

'Eh, well, I cannot see,' Philip told him in the sulks, 'why you are so put about because my sister chose to oblige your father if' (hastily) 'what you say is not the — the venomous gossip of the English court, who will always malign the French if given half a chance.'

'A whole chance, if need be,' replied Richard with that boyish grin of his.

'And *you* can't talk,' Philip peevishly continued. 'Everyone knows you've a son hidden away somewhere.'

'Not hidden,' grinned Richard, 'brought out and flung in my face — I speak figuratively — by a woman whom I met but once and now saddles me with a bastard. If I ever have a son or daughter — a son, for preference — it will be born in wedlock and my lawful heir. But I'll give you one word of warning — or, if you'd rather have it, consolation — that my brother John would not scruple to rid himself of the Gloucester girl he has taken to wife, and take to him Alais instead. A better match than the daughter of an English earl with not a drop of royal blood in her. Not that *that* is an inducement. For myself, I'd as soon we were crossed with a breed not already bred out. Back to a strain of the old Anglo-Saxons for my choice, and they too have been crossed with the

Romans who had almost all Europe and half Asia under their thumbs — or a more prolific part of their anatomies.'

'You disgust me,' whimpered Philip. 'Are you never serious?'

'I am too serious to be taken seriously, except when I carry the Cross. And as I have wasted far too much time here with you and your sister, I intend to start on my way this very noon. It is a fair nautical distance from here to Acre, travelling at five knots an hour, so I can be off at once for Sicily, and you can follow with your fleet if you feel inclined to risk pestilence and torture were you captured, and also the effect of heat in Asia Minor. So —' he hastily terminated the rest of it by avoiding Philip's unconvincing protest — 'As if *any* hazard to my life or my health would keep me from —'

'So,' Richard made for the door, 'I bid you Godspeed when you eventually go forth with your Cross emblazoned on your shield — to follow me!'

Philip did at length follow him, while Richard coasted leisurely to Naples, left there in September and rode on overland, leaving his thirty ships, to meet him and his fleet at Messina. In Salerno he heard that the main body of his fleet had overtaken him, but he was in no haste to join them; he let them go on ahead while he stayed a few more days in Salerno. He had been feeling the heat which, at that time of the year, was considerable. He therefore decided to consult the doctors of the university, then the centre of medicine in Italy.

When he learned that his entire flotilla had already reached Sicily and was awaiting his arrival, and ignoring medical advice that would have necessitated further delay before joining his fleet, he immediately travelled on with only one knight and their servants; but before he crossed the narrow Straits of Messina he halted at Bagnara. There he was told of a peasant who had a magnificent hawk. On the assumption that — as in his own kingdom — only noblemen were permitted the right to ownership of hawks, he forced an entry to the peasant's hut, seized the hawk and was at once subjected to a violent attack from a horde of angry villagers. Not knowing who this armoured robber could be they surrounded him, gesticulating and gabbling in their native dialect, unintelligible to Richard. They pelted him with sticks and stones, and one brawny fellow, evidently the owner of the hawk, swung a cudgel which might have felled him to the ground had not Richard struck back with a blow from the flat of his sword. His knight then rushed at the man with his dagger, which could have inflicted a serious injury had Richard not stayed him, saying, 'Hold! I am at fault for this.' But he was mortified to find that his sword had snapped at the hilt when with the flat of it he had laid about the fellow.

'Damnation!' he cried. 'Look here! First my staff of pilgrimage is broken, and now my sword, which could be put to better use up an infidel's arse!'

And, laughing, he received his broken weapon from his knight, who begged him, 'Pray, Sire, do not risk injury or perhaps your life with these ruffians.' Turning on them, the knight shouted, in his Norman French that was as little understood by the peasants as was their dialect by Richard, 'Do not attempt to assault the king. He is the King of —'

He was interrupted by his master: 'No! They are not to blame. I am the culprit, and as for a king, I am no king to them more than to another.' And, fumbling in his pouch, he flung a handful of coin among the crowd, who were at once in a struggling heap to grab the money. To the owner of the bird he said, 'You must keep what is yours — a fine peregrine, which is my loss and your gain.' And after a friendly wave of the hand

Richard made his escape. (He was not to escape so easily when some years later, he found himself in similar case.)

That night he crossed the Straits and slept in a tent at the foot of a mountain that sloped to the shore of Sicily. He found it difficult to sleep, even though exhausted with his journey and the incident concerning the hawk, for he was entranced by the magic of the island. Drowsily he watched the swift dark spread a bridge of dusk between night and the dying day, for there is no twilight in these semi-tropics with only the indigo sea between their golden shores and Africa.

Always sensitive to beauty either in man, woman or nature, Richard saw the crescent moon swing up above the cypress groves of the near mountains, and the plume of silvery smoke from distant Etna rising to the starlit sky; and as his eyelids drooped he murmured, 'A path of silver lies across the sea to lead me to the Holy Sepulchre.' He slept at last, undisturbed by the snores of the knight at his feet.

On the following day, when refreshed and ready for his formal entrance to the port of Messina, an eyewitness of the ceremony described the scene as: *One of pomp and splendour …* *And lo! On the horizon could be seen innumerable galleys, and from afar the sound of trumpets…*

One can well imagine the magnificence of the arrival of England's king with his ships as their oarsmen drove them forward in the foaming sea, their flags and pennons fixed to spearheads fluttering in the breeze: the vast pattern of colour, the noise, the shouting of excited onlookers, and the triumphant sky-ringing cheers as the king, in the full splendour of his state robes, appeared on a raised platform of the galley that stood foremost in the harbour. A direct contrast was this arrival of the royal Crusader to his entry at Bagnara a day or two before, unknown, unheralded, to deprive an ignorant peasant of his hawk.

But his triumphant entry into Sicily was not to be one of continuous acclaim. He could not have come to the beautiful island at a more critical time. During the twelfth century the kingdom of Sicily, then including some of Southern Italy, had been a prosperous and fertile land. Besides its luxuriant orange, lemon and olive groves it possessed an abundance of sugar cane and granaries, a country that must have been the envy and temptation of would-be conquerors. Nor were conquerors wanting through the years. As the Normans invaded England, so did their descendants invade Sicily.

But no less remarkable, as result of the struggle against invasion and conquest, was the diversity of Sicily's population. Greece had also been attracted by the opportunities offered in this Mediterranean paradise, even as far back as their ancient days when Theocritus was inspired to write his idylls for generations of poets to follow; and there on the mountains, when Richard and his Crusaders came, could still be seen a Daphnis and Chloe, and boys piping to their goats as others would see them centuries later.

Greek, Arab, Norman, each speaking their own language, all lived together in that small kingdom on the most amicable terms, but not for long. A dispute followed the death of the King of Sicily, William II, in the same year as England's Henry II had died. But unlike Henry, William had no issue. The daughter of Henry, who had married William II of Sicily, was now his widow, and Richard's sister Joan.

As Joan had not succeeded in providing William with an heir there was none but William's aunt Constance to inherit his kingdom, and she had been the wife of the German Emperor

Barbarossa. He, too, it will be remembered, had recently died of drowning while bathing in the river after an enormous meal.

But before this — which for the Sicilians was a happy accident, as they could not have tolerated a German king — they had conspired against Constance and her husband Barbarossa that the crown should pass to Tancred, an illegitimate cousin of William II. That he was a worse choice than the German they were soon to know.

A cunning, dwarfish, ugly little man, his tenure of the throne of Sicily would, as he was forced to realise, be insecure. Moreover, apart from the revolt in the mainland armies against the German accession, he was faced with Richard's Crusaders encamped within his city's walls. Worse still, King William had bequeathed to his wife Joan, Richard's sister, a handsome legacy which Tancred endeavoured to seize. He ordered the widowed queen to be kept in close confinement and withheld the dower made to her by her father before her husband's death. When Richard, on arriving in Sicily, was informed of this, he at once sent envoys to Tancred at Palermo demanding the release of his sister, to which Tancred agreed, but with the proviso that he retain her dower.

Since Henry had died before William by a few weeks, William's will had bequeathed to his father-in-law, King Henry of England, a still larger legacy than his daughter's dower which included — besides vast sums of money — a quantity of gold plate and war galleys. These Tancred now regarded as his right, and declared the will null and void.

This Richard hotly denied. He argued that William's bequest to his father had been intended to finance the Third Crusade; therefore Richard, now king, was the legal claimant to his father's legacy. The galleys alone were worth more than the money, the gold plate and a large table of gold for the use of his sister Joan. Having sent his envoys to confer with 'that bastard' Tancred, as Richard (literally) called him, he caused to be erected in Messina a gallows, sinister reminder of the punishment he would inflict upon those who demanded that the widowed Queen of Sicily should render to Tancred not only her father's dower but almost all of her late husband's wealth. Tancred, enraged at the sight of the gallows putting the fear of God and the English king into him and his islanders, seized Joan, whom he had already kept a virtual prisoner, and packed her off to the mainland with some of the gold plate he had confiscated, plus 20,000 ounces of gold. This placatory gesture was intended to heal the breach between himself and Richard. It did, in so far as Tancred offered more gold plate of Joan's dower in exchange for a marriage between his youngest daughter and Richard's nephew and heir, Prince Arthur, posthumous son of his elder brother Geoffrey.

Richard, however, having conveyed to Tancred that he would consider a marriage between these two children (and which he had no intention of considering), placed his banners on the walls and towers of Messina and proclaimed himself conqueror of the city. Tancred, seeing an advantageous solution to disturbances and riots by the future marriage of his three-year-old daughter to the child prince destined to be King of England, submitted to Richard's control of Messina.

But Philip of France, sighting Richard's banners with their leopards of gold, black and crimson waving on walls and turrets, was furious, and accosted Richard at the foot of the tower, to which men on ladders were fixing more flags. 'What,' he demanded, 'do you mean by displaying your emblems of England without acknowledging my flags? Where are my *fleurs-de-lys*? How dare you claim a captured city without conceding me my rightful share?'

'What is your rightful share?' Richard enquired lightly, with his engaging grin that served nothing to mollify Philip. 'You have sat pretty here in Messina playing chess or whatever with your pages, while I have done all the work.'

'Dirty work!' screamed Philip. 'Put up my *fleurs-de-lys* or I will tear down your godon leopards!'

Sooner than continue a wrangle in the open street with all the Greeks, Arabs and Sicilians watching and jeering at the two kings, Richard agreed that Philip's banners should be hoisted beside his own. And to ensure that he still controlled Messina he took hostages from the wealthy merchants while Tancred, having secured Richard's half-promise that the boy Prince Arthur would marry his daughter, gave Richard another 20,000 ounces of gold to be settled on Arthur's child bride when the marriage should take place.

The marriage never did take place, John saw to that; but neither Richard nor Tancred could have foreseen the murder of Arthur twelve years later.

Richard, now in possession of his father's legacy, agreed that while he remained in Sicily he would give Tancred military aid against invaders, the most imminent menace being Henry VI of Germany, successor to Barbarossa.

So far so good were these negotiations. Not only had Richard managed to recover almost all of Joan's dower, but he had captured Messina — this, however, not without fierce antagonism and violent reprisals from the Messinese, who fell upon the English, French and Norman knights whenever they saw them strolling in the streets. The Greeks — or Griffons, as the English called them — were the most bloodthirsty. The sight of Richard's banners waving on the towers caused even more fury to them than to Philip. The demonstrations, riots and attacks were renewed with such brute force that at least forty or fifty of the English — the most hated of all the pilgrim knights — were killed, while many others took refuge in the houses of the townsfolk.

This was too much for Richard. He rounded on his Crusaders in one of his tempestuous rages that astonished his friends as much as they terrified his enemies.

'You!' he roared, his voice cracking in a hurricane of anger. 'You, whom I believed to be my kingdom's strength and honour, you allow these gangs of Griffons to insult and savage us, to slay some of the best of you, to jeer and jibe at you! Do you, who take up the Sacred Cross of Our Lord, turn tail upon these Griffons — these Greeks who are crossed with the Infidel Saracens? No wonder they call us the "Long-tailed English" — yes, you! To turn your backs and show your tails to these vile crossbred mongrels!'

All this according to Ambroise, the young Norman minstrel who was one of Richard's favourites, and Hovenden, another prolific chonicler, who have left us vivid reminiscences of these Sicilian agitations. The knights, we are told, stung by Richard's tirade, roared back at him that they would follow their king to the ends of the earth and conquer all Sicily at his command.

At which Richard, a trifle less choleric, bade them: 'So be it! I take you at your word!' and rode into the city with the chastened knights behind him. At sight of the Crusaders, their shields bearing the Cross, the townsfolk scattered as they entered at the postern gates, but the knights fell savagely upon them until Richard's clarion voice rang out: 'Hold! Put up your swords! It is the city you assault, not these rats!'

Then, Ambroise records it, *might you have seen his men go up through the gates, scale the embankments and their enemies taken...* For despite Richard's orders against killing, *some,* says Ambroise, *fell foul of the knights to the number of fifty thousand citizens and others defending the walls...*

This must have been a gross exaggeration, since there could not have been more than five thousand Messinese in all; yet it is certain Richard took possession of the entire city and, again according to Ambroise, *In one attack quicker than any priest could chant matins ... And many of the citizens would have perished had not the king in his compassion spared them ...*

But as Richard's knights were not ordered to spare either the goods or the women of Messina, Ambroise records all this in one exultant *sirvente:*

And you may know of surety
That much was lost of property
When they successfully attacked
The town. It speedily was sacked
And there were women taken fair
All excellent and debonair ...

Richard, having pacified Philip by allowing his *fleur-de-lys* to be placed beside the English leopards that still billowed on the towers, insignia of his triumph, was now approached by Philip demanding an equal share of that and any future conquest. To avoid more of his grievances and grumbles, Richard agreed, but insisted he must keep the lion's share of all he yet might win. Yet Philip's share in these operations was negligible; he had hindered rather than helped with his outbursts concerning his precious *fleurs-de-lys*. 'God damn them and him!' Richard let forth to his knights. They were less tolerant of Philip and his childish tempers which, they murmured among themselves, were tricks to conceal the envy of their king, whose weakness in the past had been for Philip, the pretty youth and companion not only of his board but his bed. This caused much amused comment from Richard's friends, and malicious gossip from his enemies.

Until now Tancred had been watching and waiting for the French and English kings to settle their disputes and to decide which would be of most use to him. Finally, since Richard had conquered Messina, Tancred threw in his lot with him.

In his present pacific mood Richard silenced the incessant complaints of those knights who, having reached Messina some months before him, were sick of dawdling there caught up in the quarrels between the French and English kings. In order to compensate them for the delay in having to wait in Sicily, Richard gave *his noble knights rich gifts*, says Ambroise, *of silver and gold*...

Some of the 'noble knights' observed that the king had become increasingly uneasy as to the final success of his pilgrimage. He dilly-dallied throughout the summer, until autumn, with its equinoctial gales, decided him not to risk the sea voyage in a stormy passage. He therefore determined to remain in Messina until the spring, a decision met with the glad assent of Philip who, a deplorable sailor, loathed the sea and much preferred to travel overland than endure the torments of seasickness.

A few days before Christmas Richard, brooding on his preference for his own sex rather than for women — unless they were younger replicas of his adored mother — was suddenly conscience-stricken. Eleanor had often recounted to her son how, dressed as a man, she had escaped from her abhorrent husband and his court ... Richard, well enough read in the classics, might have likened his love for his mother to that of Oedipus.

And now, with the approach of Christmas, he felt he could not venture on the Holy Pilgrimage with a stain upon his conscience. He bethought him of his recent conquest of Messina and the ruthless vandalism of his Crusaders, but let that be the least of his sins … He worked himself into a frenzy of contrition or, as Roger de Hovenden gives it: *He called to his mind the foulness of his past life and gathered together the bishops who were with him at Messina. Falling naked at their feet to be scourged he did not blush to confess to God in their presence the thorns of his evil lusts that had grown higher than his head…* To which was added a cryptic rider: *Happy is he who after repentance has not slipped back into sin…*

However, his conscience cleared, Richard celebrated Christmas with a great feast to which he invited Philip and his nobles; and as Ambroise noted: *The rich plate was carved with precious stones — nothing cheap and common here of dirty cloths and wooden spoons,* which might indicate that before his promotion to king's favoured troubadour, Ambroise himself might often have had to submit to the 'cheap and common'.

Liberal food and wine were served, not only to the satisfaction of Ambroise but of the two kings, especially Richard who had a stronger head for libations than had Philip. So filled with the Grace of God after his confession and the scourging of his body was Richard, that he offered largesse and Christmas gifts to everyone, and to the King of France *vessels of gold and silver,* as duly remarked by Ambroise.

But despite this royal generosity the feasting did not go unmarred by broils, if not actually in the banqueting hall, then outside in the city's taverns. Some of the English oarsmen enjoying festive cheer were attacked by Genoese sailors, jealous of the warm reception given to the English who monopolised the inns, to say nothing of their women. The noise of these rows came to Richard at his feast with news that several of his men had been killed in the brawls.

'God damn them!' roared Richard. 'I'll hang the lot o' them!'

But if his objections and threats went unheeded, the next day when all were celebrating the Birth of Christ in the Church of St John of the Hospital, a Genoese or Pisan knifed one of the king's oarsmen to draw blood. Then, so Ambroise gave it, *The galleymen fell to against them and many were slain...*

We can hardly believe this brawl between English sailors and Italians from the mainland occurred within the precincts of the church, but it seems there was no truce on either side and that the English, whether or not Crusaders, were regarded as enemies by the Sicilians, Italians, and later the Cypriots when 'Richard the Unconquerable' eventually landed on their island.

THREE

The new year passed into February and enforced idleness was beginning to tell on Richard's nerves as well as on those of his Crusaders. His gossips, Hovenden and Ambroise, made much of what began as a trivial incident to end in more serious consequence.

While riding with a party of French and English knights they came upon a peasant carrying a load of bulrush canes. At once Richard stopped him and bought a few, with the idea of holding a mock tournament using the canes as lances. He was always ready for some sportive game, as if he were a boy of thirteen instead a man of thirty-three.

It seemed that while Count of Anjou, he had challenged one of Philip's knights, William de Barres, in a tournament, and got the worst of it, for de Barres unhorsed him. Richard, furious at having lost to the Frenchman, whom he thought to be nothing so good a contestant as himself, charged him again, and again he lost. As a result of this Richard took de Barres prisoner and let him out on parole. De Barres, however, broke his parole and escaped.

Richard did not easily forget an offence to the honour, not only of knighthood but of himself; and when opportunity arose to avenge what he chose to believe was an insult to the then Count of Anjou he, half in fun and more in earnest, challenged de Barres with one of the canes he had taken from the countryman. The knights, seeing in this a diversion from boredom, encircled the combatants with cheers, while Richard again laughingly challenged de Barres who rode at the king with such force that he broke off the head of Richard's cane. Instead of accepting this as a joke, Richard, still rankling at the reminder of his earlier defeat, rushed at him again, but failed to unhorse him. And now in senseless rage he charged again and again, but still the French knight kept his seat.

Then Richard's knights, who knew that the king in lighter vein loved to play the fool, began to see no foolery in this that might endanger one or both. But when the Earl of Leicester tried to intervene Richard thrust him aside, yelling, 'Let be. I'll deal with him!' And while he still failed to bring down de Barres, the king, beside himself with hot temper — his father's heritage that when roused knew no bounds — burst out with the equivalent of archaic Norman French: 'You bloody sod! Never let me see your face again until I see it on a pike, God damn you!'

And de Barres was dismissed service under Richard. Then he, rightly feeling himself wronged, took his complaint to Philip, his king and overlord. Philip, loth to take sides against Richard, to whom he had sworn fealty in their joint pilgrimage, sent the Duke of Burgundy to apologise for and beg forgiveness on behalf of his 'own puissant knight'. Richard, whose blood had now cooled, accepted the apology, relented his hasty dismissal of de Barres and recalled him to his service.

So much for that, but not enough for Philip. He had more grievance against Richard than the ridiculous affair of the bulrushes with which his 'puissant knight' had defeated the champion king of tourneys. 'The unconquerable,' sneered Philip, 'is ever a bad loser.'

We know that the betrothal of Philip's sister to Richard had been accepted as a *fait accompli* until both Richard and Alais had mutually agreed to call it off. And now Queen Eleanor had sent word to her son that she was on her way to Sicily with an alternative and more suitable bride for him than the Princess of France.

Although Richard had informed Philip of the reason why he must refuse to wed his sister Alais, it served nothing to dispel the reminder that Richard, 'his *adoré*', had dared to jilt his sister. The more Philip gnawed at the thought of it the more it splintered, as a dog's teeth will splinter a bone, till it sticks in its gullet.

Absorbed in his obsession, he took a hysterical complaint to Tancred that the King of England had insulted his sister by breaking his promise to her with whom for twenty years he had been formally betrothed. But Tancred was not to be drawn into a quarrel between the French and English kings, reviled by Philip as having cheated him —

'Me!' cried Philip, striking the air with his fist as if it were a face. 'Yes! Cheated me of my sister's right to the throne of England as consort to Richard, who cares nothing for his kingdom of England but only to fight the Saracen or some other infidel — if he ever gets to Asia. I don't give a damn about him, my dear Tancred, and I offer you my sister Alais, a far better marriage of convenience than this laughing stock. In God's name, never in my life shall I ally myself with him!'

Tancred, while endeavouring to pacify the infuriated Philip, saw here an opportunity to cement an alliance with himself and Richard against France, in addition to furthering Richard's interest in the marriage of Tancred's daughter to Prince Arthur, future King of England. Accordingly he arranged to meet Richard at Catania, where he entertained his guest right royally, offering him numerous gifts, which he refused, and a treaty of alliance that was duly signed and sealed by both.

Tancred then offered Richard four large ships of war and fifteen galleys to augment his fleet to Acre. In return Richard gave Tancred a sword purported to have been the famous Excalibur owned by the legendary King Arthur after whom his nephew and heir, Prince Arthur, had been named, though in fact it was nothing but an aged weapon adorned with suitable rust. None the less, it gratified Tancred and renewed his hope of relationship with the future King Arthur of England.

In this agreeable anticipation of honour to come, if not directly to him then to his child, Tancred accompanied Richard to Taormina. There he entertained him royally, and with fabricated diffidence and simulated hesitation produced letters he declared Philip had written to him, condemning England's king as a traitor and incapable of keeping the faith with his supposed ally.

Richard, astonished and disgusted at the treachery of the man whom he always believed had been his more than friend, despite their trifling rows, heard how Philip was urging Tancred to set upon the English king and take him unaware at night, when Philip's 'puissant' knights would join with Tancred's men to destroy him…

'By God's Throat!' This was Richard's favourite oath. 'But this is monstrous! A pack of lies. These letters are blatant forgeries contrived by an enemy or enemies of mine and of Philip. The kings of France and England, now and in the past, have always been allies and fellow pilgrims in our Crusades. And although our fathers did not actually make the pilgrimage to the Holy Land, their sons were sworn to carry the Cross! If I could find the perpetrator of these diabolical accusations I —' Richard was spluttering in one of his virulent rages — 'I — I'll

hang him with my own hands! I'll have him disembowelled —
I'll —'

'Indeed,' Tancred, trembling, strove to assure him, 'these are
no lies. The letters were brought to me by one of Philip's
envoys, the Duke of Burgundy — I can prove it.'

'Then God damn him to hell!' roared Richard. 'I know
something of this Burgundy. All grinning teeth to your face
and a dagger at your back. He hates the English as we hate
him. And as I hate you —' turning on the pale Tancred — 'for
believing in these letters that are worth less than pig's offal.
Yes, you! You are a party to causing a breach between Philip
and myself. I'll call you out for this — I'll run you through
with the very sword that was the true and trusty weapon of the
great King Arthur — I'll —'

But even as he dragged from its sheath the sword that
Tancred wore in a jewelled belt at his middle, one of the
Sicilian knights rushed forward to stay Richard's hand, begging
him to go to the French king and ascertain if the letters had
been brought by the Duke of Burgundy or the Duke's
impersonator.

'Do you *know* the Duke of Burgundy?' demanded Richard of
Tancred, who looked near to fainting with fear of him whose
height and massive frame almost extinguished the dwarfish
little Tancred.

'I — no, I did not see the Duke — one of his knights
brought me the l-letters,' he stammered.

'Then I'll take me to Philip,' shouted Richard, 'and have it
out with him. One of you is lying, and if it be you —' he
flourished Excalibur an inch or two above Tancred's shrinking
head — 'if 'tis you, there will be no treaty of alliance between
Sicily and me — only the dust and ashes of it, and of — you!'

With which parting threat, leaving Tancred staggering into the arms of his knight, Richard strode from the banqueting hall, mounted his horse and, attended by a bevy of knights, rode hell-for-leather to Messina. He burst upon Philip in his palace, once the property of a Messinese baron, and found him playing chess with one of his pages. Without any announcement, hot and dusty, travel-stained, he flung himself at the astonished Philip, and with a sweep of his gauntleted fist he overthrew the chessboard on a gold inlaid table, scattering the chessmen that they rolled broken on the polished floor. Seizing Philip by his loose embroidered sleeve he dragged him to his feet.

'Look! See this!' Richard thrust the incriminating letter under Philip's nose. 'You treacherous cur! Is this how you would uphold the Cross you have sworn to follow with me? Read it! And may God be your judge and blast you to hell!'

'King Philip, struck speechless with fear of his evil conscience,' chuckled Hovenden, who had heard Richard's noisy arrival and, with a crowd of knights, watched the row in the great hall. Hovenden had his tablets ready and was making notes, later to give full account of what followed.

With shaking hand Philip took the parchment from Richard and, motioning his page to restore the chessmen, most of which were in ruins. Bishops, queens and knights, and a king lost of his head. 'As yours will be,' shouted Richard, grabbing the ivory torso from the terrified page who was down on his knees among the pieces.

'Mine?' faltered Philip, greenly pale. 'My head —' with a hand to it as if to make sure it was still on his shoulders.

'Yes, *your* head — unless you can prove that what you have written here —' Again he snatched the parchment he had thrust at Philip. Tearing off his glove, he pointed a finger at words that danced before the dazed king's eyes. 'You would come in the night, would you, and cut me down — would you? And ally your filthy self with that bastard, the Sicilian — would you? Would you?' He capitalised the repetition of the words with a wave of the parchment over Philip's head as if it were an axe.

'N-no, I — you — have made — a mistake. It isn't true.' Philip found voice to deny. 'This mon-monstrous accusation ... not true. False. A forgery ... I swear...'

'Before God's Cross then swear it!' Richard dragged the palpitating Philip to a large silver crucifix that hung on the wall beside an arras where inquisitive heads of knights and lords were peeping. 'Swear if 'tis a forgery or the Devil's truth!'

'I — I ne-never —' Philip bowed to the ground over his praying hands, 'I swear, it is an unbelievable lie — I swear it is not true — oh, my dearest brother...' Still kneeling, he turned to clasp the leg of Richard, who stood threateningly over him. 'Will you be-believe that I — I, who loves you with all my heart —'

'Get up!' Richard commanded, 'and bring Burgundy here and let *him* swear if he did or didn't take these letters, and your villainy, to Tancred.'

Burgundy was not to be found until later that evening. He had been hawking, and when at last he came to Richard who, no longer hot and dusty, had been clothed, and if not in his right mind was not far out of it.

'Sire!' (Burgundy spoke better English than the King of England.) 'I fear Your Grace is under some serious misapprehension. The letters King Philip has shown me I have never seen. All that has been done — these letters are a — how you say — a forgery, isn't it?'

'Is it?' Richard, reclining in a deep oaken armed chair, leaped to his feet, and answered the duke in French with a raised fist, red as a ham. 'If forgeries, did you deliver them to Tancred or didn't you? Don't lie to me — I'll know the truth or you'll hang with your king for the traitor you are.'

Burgundy did not lie to him. On his oath he swore that someone — some devilish traitor who would have destroyed England's king and maligned the precious name of his *roi de France* had schemed to do this wicked mischief in order to ally himself with Tancred.

'Unless,' Richard said between his teeth, 'that bastard Tancred invented the whole thing.'

'Yes,' eagerly the duke pounced on this, 'it is possible to win your favour, Sire, that he may marry his daughter to the infant prince, your heir … isn't it?'

It was; and Richard, if not thoroughly convinced that Philip had no murderous intent to sever the alliance between them, agreed to release his 'adored brother' from any obligation to fulfil his troth with Alais — on condition, as Philip insisted, that she be amply compensated for the humiliation of being refused marriage with the King of England.

To which Richard readily allowed. Compensation in a goodly sum was offered, and Philip, determined not to run any risks that Richard might back out of his promise as he had backed out of his betrothal, issued a proclamation:

Know that all men present and to come that a firm peace has been made between us and our friend and faithful liege Richard, the Illustrious King of England of a good heart, and we will grant the aforesaid King to marry whomsoever he will, notwithstanding the covenant made between ourselves and him regarding our sister Alais whom he ought to have married…

A copy of this new treaty, as transcribed from the original French and impressively illuminated on parchment, was received by Richard with much relief but some wry comment that the words '*ought* to have married' might have been omitted. Still, he was not slow now to proceed upon his pilgrimage, unaccompanied by Philip who intended to sail for Acre in advance of his 'friend and faithful liege'.

Philip set sail for Acre at the end of March, and Richard, having escorted him along the coast of Sicily, turned back and made for Reggio on the mainland, where he was to meet his mother and 'a more suitable bride' for him than the Princess of France.

This, Richard's alternative consort, was none other than the young Berengaria, daughter of the King of Navarre.

His mother arrived with the princess and her daughter Joan, who had been lodged at Bagnara when Tancred sent her off with sundry gold plate and a gold table. Here then was the Queen Mother, full of embraces for her 'dear most precious Richard and this lovely young girl, your bride.'

The lovely young girl, his bride, did not seem to be as overjoyed with her prospective bridegroom as was the Queen Mother with her. She stood dwarfed beside the tall king of England, who towered above her little body in its cream-coloured kirtle over a blue underskirt or petticoat, her hair curling into her slender neck that rose from her low-cut corsage like — so Richard surprised himself by thinking — a rose, too pale a rose? And those eyes, those long-lashed large dark eyes as he remembered them, drooped their lids before him, and her hands were clasped together so tightly he had to take both in one of his as he bowed to raise them to his lips … *What a child it is*, came the thought, with a comical lift of his eyebrows, as he bestowed a kiss on those small clasped hands.

Her lashes lay in dark half-moons upon her cheeks as she drew away, sulky-mouthed, and offered him something as near as made no matter to a scowl. The Queen Mother and Queen Sister Joan were full of smiles, as was Richard, at what would seem to be the natural shyness of a young girl at her first introduction to one so soon to be her husband.

As for him, while still low-bowed before her from his great height and she scarcely higher than his middle, 'This,' he told himself, 'is surely child-snatching!' And to her, straightening up, he said with mock gravity, 'If it be not too personal a question to a lady who is not bound to answer — if I may make so bold as to ask — how young or how old is Your Highness?'

To which the scowl in no way lessened. 'I am old enough to be married,' she retorted, 'which is why I am here, whether I will or will not to be disposed of as if I were a — a slave! But I am of no age yet to refuse what this lady —' her underlip was pursed in a pout as she indicated the Queen Mother, not now so smiling — 'desires to do or not to do with me!' With which words, delivered in a tone of shrill defiance, she darted under the arm of the king and dashed from the room.

'Eh well! *Nom de Nom!*' ejaculated Queen Eleanor, while Richard let forth a great laugh.

'Name of a Name indeed, if so be it — of the devil, a young one, and the better to my taste than the old one!'

'A most ill-mannered child,' remarked sister Joan, who could never forget she had once been a queen. 'But what can you expect of Navarre?'

What Richard expected of Navarre was a handsome marriage portion with his daughter, sufficient to augment the vast funds necessary for his Crusade. Eleanor, having deposited the unwilling bride with Joan, set off for her journey back to

65

Normandy, thankful to have obtained for Richard 'a more suitable bride' than Alais, her late husband's mistress.

There was nothing further to delay Richard from following Philip on his way to Acre, and on 2 April 1191, Richard and his fleet sailed from Sicily. Joan and Berengaria, with their attendants, were in the first of three ships carrying the king's treasures and corn, barley and fodder for the mules and asses, to say nothing of one ship that provided for and stabled the Crusaders' horses.

The flotilla was a mighty one, numbering near upon seven hundred galleys, all set for a triumphant voyage, and Richard saw his sister and his girl bride embarking in the galley assigned to them, well manned against Saracen attack.

A fair wind carried the Armada out of the straits and into the open sea; but this fair wind was not to stay fair, for even while the king's minstrels were playing their gay tunes and Ambroise trilled a roundelay, gathering clouds darkened the crystal-clear sky with threatened storm. On Good Friday, two days after the fleet had sailed, the storm broke with a virulence so wild that superstitious sailors crossed themselves, sinking to their knees, praying forgiveness for not having stayed ashore to attend Mass on this day of the Lord's Crucifixion.

The savage gales buffeted the galleys with the king's ship leading, and huge lanterns were lighted fore and aft to guide the following ships and those that had gained alongside and ahead of his. While Richard fought the onslaught of mountainous waves that swept the deck he remained calm, cheering and encouraging his crew, but in constant anxiety as to the fate of his sister and his young bride. He had seen them sail before him, bound for Cyprus where his armada would follow, yet through the blinding curtains of mist and spray he had lost sight of almost his entire fleet.

Meanwhile Joan had retired below with her terrified women, but Berengaria stayed on deck in defiance of Joan's agonised entreaties that she must take cover or she would be drowned in the rollers that every so often engulfed the ship, riding high to drop low in the trough of the ravaging sea. 'I can feel the ship under me,' yelled Berengaria above the howl of the winds, 'as I can feel my good horse when he takes a high wall.' But her voice was less than the hum of a gnat in the thunderous roar of the gale.

To the wonder and admiration of the crew she stayed there, drenched; her hair, loosened from its circlet of gold, drooped to her shoulders and lashed her face. Her cloak was torn from her and wound itself round a broken mast. She laughed gleefully, and a young esquire to one of the knights in charge of Queen Joan and the princess laughed with her while he dragged the sodden cloak from where it clung and begged Her Highness to go below in safety. 'For,' he said, 'it be too rough, too dancherous for you here in this so bad storm.'

He spoke Norman French with a touch of English in an accent she could not identify, and she asked him if he were German.

'No,' he replied bowing; his soaked hair was a shock of reddish curls hanging in lank streaks, his leathern tunic dark with the drenching rain. 'I be of Scotland. I am sent by my king with his knights to the King of England to fight the Saracen — ' was as much of what he was attempting to tell her that she could hear, or understand. 'I am the A'Hannach, at your service, Madame.'

'Your Highness…' The captain came staggering along the heaving deck. 'I implore you…' He gesticulated wildly, since no word as he approached her could be heard. And to the

Scottish lad he made known that he must carry the princess below to join the queen and her ladies.

Before Berengaria could protest she was lifted in the young esquire's arms and borne down a rickety wooden stair to where her future sister-in-law and her ladies, suffering the throes of seasickness, were lying in miserable heaps in the tent that served as a cabin. Then Berengaria, for all her boastful courage, did at last shamingly succumb to the vicious antics of the galley where the oarsmen, fighting the desperate seas, gallantly plied the oars that miraculously withstood the fierce plunge of the waves as they drove the storm-wracked ship on and ever on through that raging maelstrom.

For three days and nights the king's fleet was at the mercy of a Mediterranean storm in a life-and-death struggle for survival. Not until the gale, as if wearied of its fury, subsided did Richard and his battered fleet anchor off Crete.

There in the tranquil waters of the harbour Richard counted those of his galleys that had followed him, and found twenty ships were missing, among them those containing his sister Joan, Berengaria and their attendants.

In his frenzied anxiety and uncertainty whether to send rescue ships in search of the lost vessels, he decided to make for Rhodes, hoping he would meet them there. He managed to reach Rhodes in safety and stayed there for three days awaiting news of the strayed ships.

The galley that had carried the women and their escorts during the great storm of Good Friday had drifted southward; and while Richard sailed past Crete toward Rhodes, another storm attacked the ships carrying the king's womenfolk and their servants. Two of these were dashed against the rocks and many of the crew in the wrecked ships were drowned. The few that struggled ashore were taken prisoner by the Emperor of Cyprus, Isaac Comnenus, at the port of Limassol.

This Isaac, self-styled 'emperor', had been sent to Cyprus as Governor for the late Byzantine Empire, and for the past six years had made himself master of the island as an independent sovereign. An ally of Saladin and fierce enemy of the Crusaders, no sooner had he sighted the pilgrim ships flying the Crusader's flag, and watched the disaster that had befallen those hapless two vessels, than he ordered his troops to seize and take prisoner the few survivors. With promise of food and shelter, the knights and members of the crew gratefully accepted the offer of help but were soon disillusioned. The emperor's men seized them, bound them and dragged them off to prison. There for a week, starving, enchained, in a foetid dungeon, they stayed where they were flung.

The galley that had kept clear of the rocks, the one with Richard's womenfolk aboard, made for the open sea and gained the port of Limassol. It was here that Isaac's 'Griffons', the Greek men of Cyprus, had captured the survivors of the wrecked ships. Joan and Berengaria now learned how the captives, despite their hunger and the injuries sustained as they struggled to shore, had found tools with which to sever their chains and succeeded in effecting an escape. They managed to find their way at night to the harbour where some of the king's ships had arrived before Richard, who was making for Rhodes. The crews of these advance galleys landed, and were engaged in fierce battle with the Griffons, finally to rout them just as the ship with Joan and Berengaria aboard her was brought to harbour.

That same evening Isaac —— who saw in the capture of England's future queen and Richard's sister hostages whereby he could receive vast sums of money for their release with

threats of death to them if the English king refused to pay —
came down to the shore, where the women and their
attendants were waiting while their servants sought shelter for
them. Greeting the two royal ladies with every appearance of
homage and dismay for their condition — in drenched clothes
and weakened with seasickness — Isaac begged they would
accept the hospitality of his castle.

Joan, however, who knew something of the tyrant
'emperor's' unsavoury reputation, refused to be his guests; but
after consultation with the captain of the galley, and urged by
the entreaties of Berengaria for a warm dry bed and change of
clothes, she feared further resistance might result in their
capture by force, as Isaac appeared to be assembling more
troops on the shore. So Joan reluctantly agreed to accept his
invitation; yet she held out for one more day in the hope that
Richard's fleet, which she knew had been making for Rhodes,
might have returned in search of them. And so it proved to be:
the next morning the galleys headed by Richard were sighted.

'Thank God,' cried Joan, taking the dishevelled and still
rebellious Berengaria in her arms. 'All now will be right, my
love!'

'All now being wrong!' grumbled her 'love', whose courage
during the worst of the storm did not accord with her
acceptance of all being right — if right it were, and if indeed
the galleys sighted afar were the king's and not an enemy's. But
as soon as he entered the harbour Richard heard of the infamy
of Isaac, and guessed what the assemblage of men and arms
ashore might portend. He immediately sent a messenger to the
'emperor' with a remonstrance for the ill-treatment of his
Crusaders. Richard was not then aware of the danger that
threatened his bride and his sister.

Isaac's troops were gathered all over his 'empire' as he grandiloquently named his usurped island of Cyprus. And when he received Richard's request he cut short the messenger with a brief insulting word. Back to the king went the message, to which Richard replied with a word equally brief and insulting, and the command to his men: '*Aux armes!*'

Between Richard's oncoming fleet, there were five of Isaac's galleys at anchor in the harbour of Limassol, and his troops ashore were drawn up behind every conceivable barricade composed of bits of driftwood, benches, shields, pieces of wreckage, metal — anything that might serve to keep the Crusaders at bay. These were all piled up along the water's edge, and behind them, rising steeply to the fortified town, stood the castle on a rock. There were no means of landing save in small boats lowered from galleys that could hold only a few men; but although exhausted after hours of sea-tossing, and encumbered by their heavy armour, the crews of each little boat plying back and forth from their galley managed successfully to combat the Griffons' army. They, if less experienced in warfare than the Crusaders, were provided with good horses and fought on their own land in the blazing heat, to which they were accustomed. Yet, while Richard's men scrambled ashore, undaunted by climatic conditions, they sent deadly volleys of arrows at the enemies' five galleys, killing numbers of their oarsmen as they landed one cockleboat after another, shooting their bolts at barricaded Griffons and their oncoming cavalry.

You might have heard them howl like dogs at us! gleefully records Ambroise in the king's ship, ever ready with his tablets — probably the first inception of a war correspondent.

But the knights and crossbowmen, with all the odds against them, captured four of the enemy's advancing galleys in a bitter fight between the two menacing fleets.

The Cypriot sailors, who had never seen the like of these armoured Franks, were terrified at the sight of them and their leader, his red hair flying in the breeze — he had discarded his helmet — and yelling orders through a trumpet from his deck. Deserting their galleys, many of Isaac's men leaped into the sea and swam for the shore. Then Richard, seeing his knights and crossbowmen returning the arrows of the Cypriot Greeks with volley after volley even though many were wounded — some fatally — dived into the sea regardless of his suit of mail to fight hand-to-hand with the escaping Griffons.

Before nightfall the Cypriots were driven back; a number of them fled helter-skelter seeking the open country. Others, panic-stricken by the advancing army of Crusaders — who had now landed troops from their ships, and were led by their king uttering fearful battle cries and wielding a formidable axe — took shelter in the hills, or in the cellars of the houses.

All this time, Isaac had been watching from a tower of his castle, and now joined his men who were in hiding, but — perceiving that his host had been routed and could not hold out against Richard's experienced iron-clad knights — he fled to the hills with Richard after him.

Ambroise, writing a ballad of this ignominious retreat to be sung to the king during the victory celebrations, gave in his account of it: *Then did you hear our men howl like dogs at the Griffons as they had howled at us...*

And still on and on came the Crusaders, their gallant crossbowmen trampling down the barricades and odds and ends collected from the hovels and houses in Limassol. Richard, tearing hotfoot after Isaac, *caught at a riderless horse abandoned by a fleeing Greek* (according to Ambroise, who must have had exceedingly long sight to have seen all this from the king's galley) *and which had only a sack for a saddle and cords for stirrups.* Mounting his runaway horse Richard shouted, 'Come on, Emperor! *Allez!* Come and joust!'

But Isaac, in no mood to joust, spurred his fleet Arab horse, Fauvel, into the mountains. There he found shelter, but Richard determined to renew the chase on the morrow and capture the 'emperor' and his island, returned to Limassol which he found bereft of Griffons. They, like Isaac, had fled before the terrible iron-clad knights and their equally terrible king, wielding an axe and chasing their emperor.

Then Richard ordered a trumpeter to proclaim: 'Oyez, Oyez, Oyez! By order of Ricardus Rex, all people of this island who did not desire or partake in war against us may come and go in safety, but such as did seek war shall have no peace or truce with us!'

One might believe that the remaining population of the island had no desire for, nor had sought any war against, the King of England. Those, however, who had fled in the wake of Isaac, and their many wounded and unable to follow, were lined up for Richard to see that they would gladly surrender in the hope of care and attention to their injuries. Richard's servants tended them, and he and his knights did hearty justice to a meal prepared in Isaac's castle.

As dawn crept over the mountains, and the reddened sky was reflected in the red-stained waters on the shore where the pilgrims and the islanders had fallen in battle, Joan and Berengaria aboard their galley, followed by the whole remaining fleet of the king, sailed into harbour. The horses in the galley, having suffered in the storm that brought the queen and princess to safety, were led ashore. The poor beasts, all stiff, benumbed and dizzy after a whole month at sea, were fed and exercised.

So ended the second day of the battle for Cyprus, with Richard's bride tucked up in a warm dry bed to sleep that whole day round until the next day's dawning.

And when the first rosy light tinged the highest mountain top Richard came in his stockinged feet to where slept his 'damozel', as his knights named her. He stood beside the bed looking down at her; she had flung off the coverings, for she, as were the fighting men, was unused to the warmth of those long May days.

So young she seemed, the merest child; her dark hair, unbraided, lay loose about her shoulders naked of her shift, which she also had found too hot. And he may have thought: *This is to be my wife — how old or — how young?* He made rapid calculation. Sixteen to his three and thirty? Young enough to be his daughter. She looked younger still than that.

As he stooped lower he felt the soft even breath from her parted lips against his cheek. He smiled as he recalled some report of her at the time of their betrothal, when brought by his mother to be handed over to his sister Joan for safe keeping, that she was 'a prudent, gentle virgin' — or, as Bertran de Born cattily remarked, '*presumably* a virgin, produced as a salubrious remedy against the great perils of fornication.' Bertran, who had spread the rumour of Richard's misbegotten son.

Then, as if she divined his thought, or in sleep became conscious of his presence, her eyelids fluttered. She stirred, and from those lips, between the halted breath of a second and a second, a name was whispered: 'Philippe…' And the lids drooped again.

With his smile still lingering, Richard tiptoed from the room. *Philippe?* Would that be a son of Flanders, he whom she had cheered at the tourney and had taken her gauntlet flung as challenge three years since, and she yet the child as he then had seen her?

But when the light of another day compelled him to arrange a surprise attack on Isaac's camp where he had hidden himself, Richard had little thought to give to the girl he must marry, whether she would or she wouldn't...

The sun stood high in heaven when, with fifty knights, he set out for the mountains where five miles away was the emperor's camp. They were all asleep after the heavy fighting and hardships they had suffered chased by Richard's army, as reported by his scouts.

Ambroise, who had left the king's ship and now following the king and his main force, was in his element later to record: *With a great terrible cry the king entered the tents while the exhausted enemy lay as if dead and the king's army fell on them like ravening wolves...* In his exultation Ambroise turned from zoological similes as the *howling of dogs* and *the ravening of wolves* to the elements when Richard *charged the foe more swiftly than a thunder bolt...*

Driving full tilt through the camp, striking right and left with his great battle axe and yelling his formidable war cries, no wonder the Greeks scattered in confusion. *When the main body of the king's troops came up they butchered the Greeks in their tents ... No man knew the number of the dead...* gleefully sang Ambroise. For a troubadour who delights in tuneful roundelays and *sirventes*, he was uncommonly bloodthirsty, and may have anticipated a knighthood for his courageous records in the fighting front of the king's equally bloodthirsty hosts. Richard was known to be prodigal of knighthoods.

The surviving Griffons were chased into the mountains, some on horses, most on foot, and among them the Emperor Isaac on his fleet Arab charger. He took refuge behind the rocks of the precipitous mountain paths. Richard had not yet succeeded in taking Isaac prisoner, but he did strike down the emperor's standard bearer; then, giving up the chase, he returned with his army to Limassol.

On the way back to the town his knights and men took from Isaac's tents their booty of gold and silver plate; and from the emperor's bed much 'silken stuff', which Ambroise may have confiscated for his own: *Horses and mules laden with hauberks, helmets and swords; oxen and kine, nimble goats and ewes aplenty, and mules with embroidered cushions for their backs...* All this handed out to Richard's knights and men, and we may be sure that Ambroise was not forgotten nor lacked an embroidered cushion for his own back.

Before the king retired to a well-deserved rest after a good meal, a message was brought to him announcing that the titular King of Jerusalem, Guy de Lusignan, had arrived with three leading Crusaders to pay homage to England's King. He also tactfully suggested that he sought the support of King Richard against King Philip Augustus of France.

From the somewhat ambiguous information accorded him in the letter, Richard gathered that Philip, who had reached Acre several weeks earlier, was preparing to depose Guy de Lusignan in favour of Conrad de Montferrat, a handsome young man whom the susceptible Philip much preferred to the elderly, unprepossessing Guy. Richard was none too pleased at being dragged into a situation against his ally Philip in a partisanship with de Lusignan, of whom he knew little yet enough to judge him a difficult customer with whom to deal, albeit an ardent Crusader. However, it had come to his knowledge that Guy had brought with him three galleys well stocked with armaments and provisions. All grist to the mill of his armies, since he had lost, as he feared, a number of ships in the storm.

None the less, he felt much aggrieved when, having already begun to undress for his bed, he must go down to meet Guy in his galley just come to anchor in port.

'By Holy Cross and St Mary!' swore Richard. 'I am in no mood to parley with Guy, deposed or not, and have Philip on my track for taking sides against him!' However, down to the harbour he went with three or four knights and the ubiquitous Ambroise, not to be done out of an interesting rencontre with this de Lusignan.

Gossip or legend gave it — as Ambroise was well aware and would recount in amusing ballads — that Guy de Lusignan, of an ancient Poitevin house, had descended from one Melusine, wife of Raymond de Lusignan. She had the reputation of having transformed herself, on every Sabbath eve, into a serpent from the waist downward. Whether she attended Mass in this singular duality was not known, but what was known, or was claimed to be vouched for, was that she eventually ended up as a dragon. These diverse changes of identity must have greatly alarmed her husband, to say nothing of his descendants, many of whom — Guy in particular — cared not to be reminded of extraordinary phenomena attached to his ancient and honourable name that might, at any future time or even in his present time, recur either in himself or his children.

'Let us hope,' the irrepressible Ambroise was overheard to say, 'that he will not breathe fire on us if he should revert to his great-great-greatest grandmother while we visit him!'

Richard may have uneasily wondered something of similar sort when, bone weary after his arduous day chasing Isaac and his Cypriots, he could have wished Guy at the bottom of the sea instead of afloat upon it when rowed out to de Lusignan's ship.

The sinking sun had set fire to the sky in its glorious cremation to turn the vivid blue of the Mediterranean to a darkening red-shotten purple. Affecting a cordial welcome, Richard invited his guest to the castle; and was relieved when he conducted him to his apartment that no serpentine or dragonish symptoms were, so far, manifest in the mail-coated body of Guy de Lusignan.

'Sleep well and God be with you,' devoutly did Richard bid him goodnight; but he thought it best to have a watch put on the door, and buckets of water in readiness should smoke or smell of burning or sight of flame issue from the room where Guy would pass the night. We must remember that Richard, though a valiant Christian Crusader, was born in a superstitious age and fully believed in demons, witches, the devil in various forms, and, with a knowledge of Grecian mythology, still could credit the transformation of human beings into some fabulous animal or monster.

However, nothing of alarm issued from the apartment where Guy was couched, other than resounding snores that, even to the credulous and apprehensive guards, could not be mistaken for anything superhuman.

The next day brought the promise of uninterrupted sunshine for the wedding of King Richard Plantagenet of England to the Princess of Navarre.

FOUR

Still almost a child, seeming less than her sixteen years, she was awakened by her maids and her soon-to-be sister, Joan.

A gown had been salvaged from the sea-sodden baggage to provide her with raiment befitting a queen. White satin, lavishly embroidered, clung to her small body close as a glove, scarcely defining the slight swelling of her breasts. Her hair, entwined with pearls from Joan's jewel caskets, was braided beneath a cap of silver gauze, and from it suspended a veil of exquisite lace.

Pale as the whiteness of her gown was she, her eyes behind the transparent veil two dark pools that held no light, only a frightened wandering stare as if she sought some face, some friend, someone who had known her before she had been launched upon this strangest of adventures. Marriage! And all this, she must have thought, following near upon a shipwreck! And here was he, the man, the king to whom she had been brought and delivered 'as if she were a slave'... A giggle rose to her lips, red as if they had been painted in contrast to the pallor of her face. He, the man she was now about to marry, strode up the aisle of the chapel in the castle of Limassol, which Richard had appropriated for his own.

The wedding service conducted by King Richard's chaplain, Father Nicolas, was immediately followed by the coronation of Queen Berengaria. This, performed by the Bishop of Evereux, was a speedy affair, having none of the glamour usually associated with a crowning. For indeed there was no crown to place upon the head of Berengaria, Queen Consort of England.

The elaborate insignia of queenship, which should have been packed in the king's luggage along with his own wedding robes, had either been forgotten or mislaid in the confusion of his arrival from Rhodes and the search for his bride and his sister during the storm that might have lost them both to him for ever.

These ceremonies over, there then began a wedding feast that lasted long into the night. Because of the severe fighting in the attack upon Isaac and his Greeks that had caused the Crusaders so many deaths and casualties, with the wounded lying in the apartments of the castle, the company was sadly depleted. But those who sat at the nuptial board to toast the king and his bride did not allow the thought of their comrades' sufferings to interfere with the good food and plentiful wine purloined from the emperor's cellars.

Richard, we are told, was 'jocose, affable and glorious on this happy occasion', which is more than could be said of his queen. In her white bridal robe, pearl-embroidered, her face, no less white under the circlet of gold that served for a crown, showed nothing that was affable, jocose or glorious. This is scarcely surprising when she, the spoilt darling of her father and his court, had endured the perils of the sea and the ordeal of her wedding with no kith or kin to support her, and then the confusing procession for her crowning: the guards and men-at-arms following her to the blare of trumpets as she was led by her bridegroom to kneel before the bishop. Never having attended a coronation, she could not know how unceremonious was this, as if it could not be over and done with too quickly. The mumbling of the bishop, the loud and incomprehensible responses of her husband, the prompting of his chaplain who stood at her side murmuring in her ear the words she must say in Latin, of which she understood no more than had it been in Hindustani, filled her with a sense of unreality akin to nightmare.

And now here she was, seated at a board laden with dishes of gold and silver and in a country inhabited by savages, as she believed the Greeks to be, in their outlandish garments, armoured to the waist and wearing petticoats exposing naked legs, as she had seen when she watched from a window in the castle. And how they had yelled and shrieked, uttering unintelligible war cries as they advanced or retreated from Richard's Crusaders. Then to be dressed in these trappings and married to a man twice her age and almost a stranger, with whom she had exchanged not half a dozen words since her first meeting with him in Sicily!

She could but vaguely remember how long ago — for to sixteen three years is long ago — she had sat beside this very large and loud-voiced man at a tourney in Navarre. And this same man, between plying her with wine, vociferously responded to the toasts of his knights and courtiers while his minstrels played on harp and lyre. There were two or more of them, including Ambroise, of course, and another whose name she did not know, a pretty youth whom she afterwards learned was one Blondel, a favourite minstrel of the king. He had been kept in safety as far as possible during the fighting, before the king's galley deposited him on the island.

There was yet another at the table, with its luxurious appointments of gold and silver looted from the emperor's tents, who caught her eye with unmistakable recognition in his spreading smile. He, she saw, was the Scot with the bush of reddish hair and a round jolly face, pink as that of the cherubs depicted in the frescoes of the vast banqueting hall. How had he named himself when, as ordered by the captain of the storm-tossed galley, he had carried her below? The Hannsomething, was it? No matter. She would be unlikely ever to know or speak to him again. He was no knight, only the esquire of one of them.

The king had an arm around her shoulders while he roared in her ear, 'Why so solemn, my dear? You must rise to our guests. Get up and reply to the toasts in your honour...' which was as much as she could understand of his Angevin French.

So here was something more to confuse and dismay her! To be made to 'get up' from the board among all this shouting company of men — not a woman among them except Queen Joan, all smiles and nods, making faces at her to speak. To whom must she speak? To the king whose arm, strong as a bear's, hugged her again as she was bidden, 'Get up! Tell them how happy you are to be...'

'Why,' she interrupted, 'am I supposed to be happy?' But this went unheard in the deafening cheers and roars that accompanied the king's attention to his pale little queen. Raised from her seat she heard herself say — if it were herself, and not a lost soul speaking in a nightmarish hell for the sin of defiance against marriage with a man, king or nothing, whom she hardly knew — 'I am pleased I am here to greet you, *Messires*, who is your wife — I mean —'

What *did* she mean? And why more roars of laughter poking fun at her who could not speak their English or their Norman French, and so noisy to make her head spin ... yes, this was surely hell's punishment for disliking him who at the altar had vowed, in so much as she could understand of the priest's Greek or Latin, to worship her with his body, whom she must obey in sickness and in health. Sickness. Yes! And sick did she feel, with her head in a spin from the wine he had made her drink, refilling the golden goblet that the walls of the banqueting hall raced round her as if she were back in the

galley with the ship bouncing on the waves so she must fall ...
and fall she did. O, horrors! To sprawl across the cloth and
into the silver dishes, splashing gravy on her white satin gown
... More laughter and loud applause from them all, and from
him when he lifted her up in his arms, laughing, to tell her, 'We
must teach you better how to hold your liquor, my darling...'

O shame, O misery! Disgraced. She was carried from the
table in the arms of this large man, her husband, the king or
the devil, for surely the devil was in it to make her so
shockingly drunk!

Her cheek against his gold-embroidered tunic was pricked as
with pins and needles. He had dressed himself magnificently
for his marriage in a tunic of *rose coloured samite and a mantle
bedight with shining orbs like suns*, as Ambroise noted, not perhaps
without some envy. But Berengaria was too far gone to notice
or to envy her bridegroom's gala dress: more than that, the
'sun-like orbs' had grazed her face as she was borne to her
bedchamber, disrobed by her maids, with Queen Joan tut-
tutting at the ruin of her gown. 'And the pearls half drowned in
gravy. Go, Richard. Go away while I prepare her for you. Why
on earth did you make her drink that wine? I warned you not
to give her this vile strong Cyprian stuff. There, then, there, my
poor little one.'

Between soothing pats and strokings of her 'poor little one',
Joan drove her brother from the room to tell him, 'No, not
tonight. She is in no fit state — you must let her sleep. She has
not yet recovered from that dreadful voyage, which was all but
the death of us both.'

So, couched between silken sheets, her head splitting, her
stomach turning, this hitherto youngest of English queen
consorts slept on her wedding night and, thankfully, alone.

There were many more nights for Richard's young queen to pass alone among strangers, save for Queen Joan. And she was poor company, for ever bemoaning her lot at being held a virtual prisoner on 'this godforsaken island', while her brother pursued his chase of Isaac to force his surrender of Cyprus.

On the day after his wedding and the coronation of his wife she was found to be suffering from a tertian fever, according to Father Nicolas. He, who had some knowledge of medicine and could treat bodies as well as souls, advised that the queen remain in bed until the fever passed. Richard was adjured not to assert his conjugal rights while his wife's condition necessitated complete rest after her stormy sea passage and the subsequent ordeal of her coronation.

Richard, not a little relieved that he must postpone his marital obligations, which he guessed were unlikely to be welcomed, was only anxious to continue his pursuit of Isaac and the ultimate capture of Cyprus. Having made a marriage settlement upon his wife of the lands of Mans, he assembled the reinforcements brought by Guy de Lusignan, and determined to conquer Cyprus since the island lay across the supply route to Jerusalem and was of paramount importance to his Crusade.

Isaac, who had taken refuge in Nicosia, the capital of Cyprus, perceiving that nothing could be gained by further defiance, sent word to Richard that he wished to discuss terms of peace. Richard and his knights then rode out to the meeting between himself and his enemy, the 'emperor'. It took place in a garden of fig trees between the harbour and the road to Limassol.

Ambroise, ever ready with his tablets, following in the wake of the king and his knights, records that Richard had dressed himself in all his wedding finery, *girt with a well proved sword, a silken belt, a finely chased scabbard edged with silver.* (Richard, always meticulously point device, was the more so when out to impress.) Mounted on a magnificent Spanish horse, his spurs, Ambroise noted, *were of gold, his saddle red-studded with little golden stars, and having on its hinder part two golden lion cubs rampant, snarling at each other…*

We can imagine the scene in that garden under a sapphire sky with the sun pouring down upon the heads of the two kings in conference: the one, Isaac, well accustomed to the heat of a Cyprian May day, and Richard, sweating in his elaborate gala dress, his fiery hair concealed beneath a red cap, no less red than his face from which sweat drops trickled from his forehead to his beard.

Isaac, realising there was nothing to be gained for the present (with the mental reservation he would see this Frankish Richard damned before he would surrender his island kingdom), promised fealty — not, we hope, snarling, but in honeyed words — exchanged the kiss of peace and agreed to hand over all his castles and his imperial domains of Cyprus with the enormous indemnity of three thousand five hundred marks and the promise of five hundred knights to accompany him on his Crusade to the Holy Land.

So far so good; but Richard had reckoned without his host. Isaac had laid his plans and, while offering his kiss, had no intention of keeping his pledge of fealty or his lavish promises.

Richard, who, incredibly, had taken him at his word, retired to the castle for the night. This was the chance for which Isaac had been waiting. He mounted his splendid horse Fauvel, and rode like hell to his palace at Famagusta on the east coast.

Richard, having heard that Isaac's Fauvel could outspeed any horse of his own or his army's, decided to sail at the head of his galleys and land at Famagusta where his troops, under Guy de Lusignan, awaited him. When he arrived there he found the palace deserted. Then did he know how he had been deceived by the cunning Isaac.

After sending some of his ships to guard other coastal towns against Isaac's escape, Richard stayed on at Famagusta for a day or two to give audience to envoys sent from Philip demanding that he would at once proceed to Acre, which the French king had already reached, and was waiting for Richard to join him.

This message Richard much resented for its peremptory command from one who, although his ally, he considered to be his lieutenant and he the superior officer in their Holy Pilgrimage. According to Ambroise he returned Philip a message in words so insulting that they were *not herein to be set down*. What these words were that Ambroise, never as a rule too squeamish to write unrepeatable language used by his choleric master, we may guess; but we know that Richard swore, 'By God's Throat! not for all the wealth of Russia would he leave Cyprus until he had conquered the island and that (unprintable) bastard Isaac.'

Meanwhile the 'bastard' had ensconced himself in a great fortress perched high on a mountain in the north of Cyprus. This, as legend gave it, purported to be the Castle of Love built for Cupid by Aphrodite, the Cyprian risen from the sea. In this romantic stronghold Isaac, confident that Richard would give up his fruitless chase and proceed to the Holy Land, remained in safety — as he thought.

He was mistaken.

Leaving his Castle of Love, that more appropriately might have been named the Castle of Hate, Isaac returned to Nicosia, thinking that Richard had left the island to join Philip at Acre.

Caught in a trap with his household troops panicking at the advance of the merciless Franks and their leader, Isaac attempted unsuccessfully to harass Richard's vanguard, and did himself shoot two poisoned arrows at the king, but missed him.

In renewed fury Richard dashed after Isaac and would have taken summary vengeance for attempted murder, but Isaac mounted on Fauvel outrode him and took refuge in another of his castles, the fortress of Kyrenia. Here he had placed his wife and little daughter out of harm's way, unaware that Guy de Lusignan had gone ahead of him to storm the castle and take prisoner Isaac's wife and child.

Beside himself with grief at the loss of this little one, Isaac heartbrokenly surrendered. His one hope now was to have restored to him his beloved only child. For his wife he cared nothing, having had many willing substitutes during his usurpation of Cyprus.

Flinging himself at the feet of Richard, the possessor of his castle and the whole of the island, he was graciously received; but while Richard agreed to save his little daughter, he gave Isaac no assurance that he would allow him his release. Instead he ironically conceded him in regard, as he said, for his royal rank, that he would not be put in irons (the common lot of all prisoners) but enchained in silver. This done, he was despatched under the guardianship of Guy de Lusignan to the nearest point on the Syrian coast: Tripoli.

Having promised Isaac the safety of his daughter, Richard placed the child in the care of his sister Joan, to be sent with Berengaria to Jerusalem.

So with a fleet of a hundred and sixty, their number increased by some of the Cyprian navy and Guy de Lusignan's three convoys, Richard left Cyprus in the first week of June.

Winds were fair and the king in the leading galley sailed past the white city of Tripoli and the terraced castles of Botron, overlooked by the Knights of St John. Then suddenly, between Beirut and Sidon, there was sighted an enormous ship approaching Richard's galley. The sailors, crossing themselves for fear, believed it to be a spectre of evil. Some of them, crowding for a closer view, thought that nothing of so great a size had ever sailed a sea since Noah's Ark.

As she drew near they saw she carried three masts, and that one side of her was green, the other yellow. Her whole appearance was so strange and awesome that the superstitious declared it to be the work of witchcraft, sent by Saladin to sink the king's armada.

The more courageous hailed her to ask who she was and whence she came, and were answered in Norman French: 'We are Genoese bound for Tyre.'

The majority were relieved to know that this sea monster meant no harm to them, but one of the oarsmen spoke aside to Richard, 'Sire, hang me if she be not a Turkish ship, bound not for Tyre but for mischief!'

'And hang me,' retorted Richard, 'if you are wrong, for I have seen such a one as this — a Turk, by God — laden with victuals and supplies at Beirut. Bring up another galley,' he roared to the nearest of his following fleet, 'and close in, but do not hail her.'

This order, promptly obeyed, was greeted with a violent shower of bolts and arrows from the Turk, causing instant casualties among the Christians. Seeing how some of his men seemed to waver at this assault, so swift and murderous, Richard swore he would hang the lot of them if they let the Turk escape.

The threat had the desired effect to bring renewed attack by the storming party; despite the rain of arrows, they managed to clamber aboard the Muslim ship, though many of them were driven back. Those who could not get away were seized, brutally slaughtered, their hands and feet cut off, and their bodies thrown into the sea. While Richard's men rescued those not too severely injured to survive, several others were drowned.

'God damn the Infidel!' swore Richard. 'I'll scupper her!'

He gave the order for divers to swim under her and secure her rudder with ropes, while again an assault was made by his men with more butchery of his knights and seamen. Richard then commanded the two leading galleys to ram the Muslim ship and make a breach in her side and keel. This unexpected onslaught, taking the Turk by surprise, created panic as the sea rushed in to flood her. While every endeavour was made by the Muslims to staunch and bale the flood that rapidly swamped her below and poured on her above, the doomed ship, torn open, heaved over and sank. Those of the Turks caught in the deluge jumped overboard to be shot by the Christians' arrows or drowned. Richard and his men saved thirty-five of their emirs; the rest were left to their fate.

It had been reported by one of Richard's galleymen that about two hundred 'poisonous ugly grey serpents' were aboard the Turk's ship, to be let loose when they boarded the king's galley and to kill him and his pilgrims. But Richard laughed this to scorn and said it must have been a serpentine contrivance for throwing fire, since bottles of inflammatory stuff were found among the wreckage.

The sinking of the Saracen ship was Richard's first outstanding success in his pilgrimage to the Holy Land, for had the Turk reached Acre with its plentiful stores of food, ammunition and equipment, the city might never have been taken.

During the last two years Acre had been under siege, and thousands of Crusaders killed or lost by disease, or shipwreck on the way. These incalculable numbers may have been exaggeration as reported by contemporary chroniclers; none the less, as Gibbon gives it: *Never did the flame of enthusiasm burn with so fierce or more destructive a rage...* This fierce, destructive rage was doubtless inspired by Richard in his determination to conquer the Infidel and win back for the Christians the Holy Sepulchre.

Fair winds, which at the conclusion of the sea battle had turned unfavourable, now changed again to favour Richard's fleet and carry the victorious galleys to Tyre. Brought within sight of the towers and minarets of Acre rising out of the sun-dazzled sapphire sea, *Around Acre,* sang Ambroise, *were camped the flower of all the peoples of the world...* As usual this romantic's imagination ran to fantasy that the king's favourite young minstrel, Blondel, always at Richard's beck during his hours of relaxation, might set to music the versified twitterings of Ambroise.

Since less than half of the world had been discovered by intrepid explorers eight centuries ago, not all the besiegers of Acre were Crusaders. Before Richard other Crusaders had besieged the Sultan's formidable Muslims, for Saladin had at his command an unlimited supply of men and arms.

The Christians' camp, with Philip, had arrived some two months earlier than Richard to await the arrival of the English king with reinforcements. And when Richard reached Acre with his armies in June, *Then had you heard the trumpets sound honouring Richard, the Knight without peer!* declared Ambroise joyously. *Not any mother's son hath seen or could describe such rejoicing as was made over the king...* The whole camp blazed with the light of innumerable tapers and torches, while roundelays accompanied by clarions, flutes and Blondel's harp were lost in the general uproar to hit the sky and bring the seagulls screeching their dismay at this unprecedented row as they circled above Acre. But the singing and shouting of the besiegers without and within the beleaguered city, gave the Saracen armies no cause for rejoicing.

Saladin, seeing from his retreat on the hills these hordes of Crusaders blocking all entrance to and exit from the city, realised that unless he could draw off the advancing Christians it would mean starvation for the garrison.

Meanwhile Richard, notwithstanding his triumphant descent upon Acre, was met with less jubilation from Philip than he might have expected. On his arrival at Acre some two months before, Philip, in his own estimation, had been the leader of the Third Crusade; but with the coming of Richard he looked to be relegated to the second-in-command with all honours and laurels of victory bestowed upon his ally, the English king.

When he had been first in the front of the siege, Philip had taken possession of two towers. One had been named by the Roman conquerors the 'Tower of Flies', having been the altar where sacrifices were offered to the gods. It stood on a rock above the city and had been the haunt of flies voraciously feasting on the sacrificial carnage. The second fortress which Philip claimed as his, called the 'Accursed Tower', was the largest in all Acre's fortifications. Situated on the wall surrounding the city, it had been so named by the Knight Templars, since legend gave it that the thirty pieces of silver for which Judas had betrayed Our Lord had been found there.

Day in, night out, Philip bombarded this tower with heavy blocks of stone. While Saladin's Muslims on the high lands beyond the city strove to engage the Christians on the plains, the Crusaders and some of the Muslims — who had come to believe in the Christian God as more powerful than Allah — helped to fill in the ditch or moat that circled the walls with great stones and rocks or the bodies of animals.

Undeterred by the ceaseless rain of arrows and buckets of boiling pitch thrown at them by the Turks, the fanatical Crusaders — urged by Philip, who saw himself the Saviour of the Holy Land — toiled in rivers of flame and the appalling stench of putrefying bodies under a glaring sun. But this large-scale attack from the besiegers was met with frenzied counter-attacks by Saladin's Muslims, pouring down from the hills to fling themselves upon Philip's Crusaders in bloody hand-to-hand fighting. Yet even when driven back again and again the fearless Saracens managed to prevent further advance of the Christians.

It was under these conditions that, despite his confidence and self-esteem, Philip lost heart and, overcome with fury and disappointment that he had been unable to take possession of the city for all the gallant efforts of his Crusaders, fell into what was then described as 'a languid sickness from sorrows', but more likely resultant from the stench of strewn corpses in the broiling heat. Such was the case of his ally when Richard, attended by tumultuous shouts of greeting and homage, arrived on the scene.

There were more sick sorrows and inward fury for Philip, who, striving to meet the English king with similar welcome, stifled his jealousy at the evident delight with which Richard's coming had been received by all, French and English alike. More than ever did Philip inwardly fume to see his Crusaders, led by the Duke of Burgundy and Count Philippe of Flanders, hurling great rocks and stones over the fortifications to strike terror among the Turks, urged on by Richard waving his huge battle axe with yells of encouragement to the knights and Hospitallers.

We must admit that Richard did all he could to increase his own popularity and to undermine that of Philip, no less than did the French king claim supremacy over him of the Lion Heart. When he discovered that Philip had been paying his men three gold bezants a month, the equivalent of a guinea each, Richard offered four bezants a month to any knight who would serve under him, no matter whether he were Pisan or Genoese; but while the Pisans eagerly accepted the offer — or bribe — the Genoese loyally serving the French king refused it.

With mounting hostility and a recurrence of his 'languid sickness' Philip watched the English king, 'this godon Richard', and saw how he took command of, and was obeyed by, not only his own men but also Philip's! *How much longer?* he asked himself, while in a fever he tossed on his bed in his surrendered Tower of Flies — at least he could claim to be master of that, notwithstanding the stink of bodies rotting in the airless heat. How long, O God, how long must he endure this hell-hound, 'the Lion Heart' — be damned to him whose Templars and Hospitallers were armoured with far more effective slings to hurl heavier rocks at the Saracens than any of his own trusty followers...

Uneasily he watched the English king, who had brought with him the enormous wooden tower called Mategriffon which had been built to overawe the Greeks and Lombards during his siege of Cyprus. Richard had reassembled it and set it up to strike terror in the Muslims with fear of him and of their Allah.

While all this was happening at Acre, Richard's wife and sister, in charge of Isaac's child, had been sent on in advance to Jerusalem but were unwilling to reach Palestine before Richard.

Their galley and their two convoys did, at Joan's command, change course to slow down and follow in the wake of the Crusaders.

Keeping well in the rear of Richard's fleet, the ship of the two queens had escaped encounter with the Turkish galley believed by the Christian seamen to be a second Noah's Ark. As they approached Acre Joan ordered the captain of her ship to lie off beyond the harbour, where Richard had been greeted with an uproarious welcome of bonfires and brilliant illuminations turning night into day. This greatly appealed to Berengaria, who delighted in such jubilant relief from the miseries of a stormy passage. She stood in the bows of the galley, gently rocking at anchor in that peaceful sea, and saw the night sky as if on flame, with the moon a red-gold lantern among a galaxy of golden stars. Only when Joan, less enthralled than was her brother's bride (still 'presumably a virgin') by these joyous celebrations, persuaded her to go to bed, did Berengaria reluctantly obey.

'It is near dawn,' Joan, who was half asleep and yawning, told her, 'and I cannot stay awake all night. I am not so young as you.'

'I want to see the fireworks — look! They are shooting great wheels of light up to the moon!'

'There will be fireworks and celebrations enough for you when we meet Richard in Jerusalem,' Joan said with rather more conviction than she felt. For knowing her brother, 'Yea and Nay', she guessed he would be in two minds whether or not to alter course again for Tyre (where he had been forbidden by Conrad of Montferrat's guards to open gates for him). She knew Richard would make every effort to overcome Conrad who, under Philip's auspices, had taken to himself too much honour as Lord of Tyre from whom Richard, she believed, would wrest that privilege as his own right. All, Joan told herself, would not be plain sailing for Richard before Jerusalem and the Holy Sepulchre were his.

Meanwhile Berengaria, having been put to bed, slept the sound sleep of youth and was awakened in the morning by one of her women with a basket of fruit. This was more a surprise for Berengaria than for Joan, who likewise had been given a basket of woven gold — as it looked to be — with the compliments of the Sultan Saladin to the gracious Lady Jehanne, Queen of Sicily. What did this gesture portend, she wondered? And how did Saladin know that she and Richard's wife were anchored here? Certain he had his Muslims — spies, no doubt — swarming round the ships on the harbour, merchantmen from all quarters bringing goods to sell and also to buy the wine, spices, fruit and sweetmeats offered by a clamorous throng of men and boys in rickety little boats. Doubtless some of these, ever on the watch for Saladin's enemies the Knights of the Cross, had reported the arrival of the royal galleys bearing such tempting hostages, if captured, as King Richard's sister and his wife!

One begins to suspect one's own shadow, Joan told herself, and was inclined to forbid Berengaria to eat of the fruit, for what if the Infidel Sultan had thought to poison the two Christian queens?

But Berengaria, sitting up among her pillows, was already sucking the juice of a large lemon-coloured globe unlike any fruit seen before. 'It is a giant orange!' she cried as Joan entered the cabin.

Relieved that the girl did not turn pale and vomit, Joan ventured to taste of the luscious fruit, twice the size of an orange, to find it, if a trifle sour, most refreshing. A grape fruit was most likely then unknown in the orange groves of Navarre or Sicily.

Having breakfasted, Berengaria was again at her post in the bows. But now the battle for Acre was in full force. The sky, cleared of the fires that had looked to burn the moon on the previous night, was filled with sun-dazzle that pointed with diamond sparks the gay little ripples of the sea.

'What sea is this?' she asked the captain who, never far from her, was watchfully alert for her safety. On the distant coast could be seen in that clear clarified air countless small, mailed figures swarming on the shore, climbing the cliffs where stood the great dark towers, and every so often could be heard the roar of falling rocks and battle cries, the clangour of steel and the screams of wounded horses and men as Crusaders and Muslims fought hand-to-hand, either mounted or on foot.

The captain, proud of his knowledge, was explaining to the king's young queen. 'It is the sea of the Levant, Madame, that lies between the southern coast of Europe and northern Africa. And here Your Grace can see far distant to Damascus, where Saint Paul saw the Light and was sworn to follow Him who we now do follow…'

She was not listening. She had leaned forward, her hands gripping the rail of the turret which in these twelfth-century ships were built at the bows and stern of a galley from where archers could take aim with bowshot at close range. The captain eyed her anxiously. Her hair, loosened from the fillet that bound it, drifted across her eager little face to be swept impatiently aside.

'See!' She turned to grab the captain's arm. 'If my eyes do not deceive — I am very long of sight — do I see in the forefront of those knights — our knights surely? — for I can see the white cross on their shields — and I can see —' she shaded her eyes with a hand — 'I can see the crest on the helmet of my cousin Philippe of Flanders. He is of the French king's Knights of the Cross. Oh!' She lowered her hand to clasp it with the other. 'I pray he will be safe — he is the brave knight who fought in a tourney when I first met the king, my husband … I was then only … oh!' Her voice rose to a scream. 'It looks like the king has fallen. I know him by his great battle axe.'

Joan, who had come to stand beside her, bade the captain close in nearer the shore. 'If the king is wounded or —' her voice dwindled but, gaining firmness, resumed — 'I and my women must be beside him and the injured. There are only men to attend them…'

Many were the injured and dead among Muslims and Christians alike, suffering as much from the stench of putrefying corpses as from their wounds. But Richard had not been killed as Joan dreaded to have heard. He was carried from the battle by his faithful minstrel Blondel and by Ambroise, forsaking his tablets to attend him in his tent. Richard and his men were protected in their encampment by barricades of turf, bags of sand and driftwood from the shore. It was here that Joan ordered the captain of the queens' galley to land her and her women, much against the captain's judgment. He feared the king's wrath for allowing his womenfolk to risk their lives under the ceaseless attack of Turkish archers in reply to formidable assaults from the Templars hurling their deadly torrents of stones and rocks. Yet, disregarding the captain's advice, Joan — accompanied by Berengaria who refused to be left behind in the galley with Isaac's child — insisted on going to the tent where Richard lay in parlous plight. His wounds were trifling, 'mere scratches,' he muttered, for he had been well armoured from head to foot, but divested of his headpiece it was seen that his face and lips, as Ambroise reported, *were all wasted by a sickness called leonardie.*

This ailment, so named by the physicians of those days, may have been a virulent form of malaria as described in the works of Hippocrates, had they been able to obtain a translation from the Greek, which is unlikely. But we must take the word of the doctors in attendance on the king and his armies that a peeling of the skin, the loss of hair and the nails of hands and feet were the complications of the fever. His armour having become unendurably heavy, he had finally dropped from exhaustion when Berengaria had seen him fall.

Unable to take an active part in the battle for Acre he lay in impotent fury, 'imprisoned', he raved, 'by my sister and my queen!' Not that Berengaria had much to say or to do with the nursing of him, save to get in everyone's way, and continually to enquire if his hair, which was thinning to leave bald patches, would ever grow out again, until Joan in exasperation ordered her back to the galley, an order she obstinately refused to obey. She did, however, leave the tent to sit outside in the debris and rubble watching the incoming tide on the white sands of the shore and wishing, not for the first time, that she had never set eyes upon this English king. Heart of the Lion, as they called him, and less of a lover than a stranger 'who never so much as comes near me more than to kiss my hand,' she told herself. And as for his handsome looks, which her father would always be praising, she had seen better-looking bullocks drawing carts from the vineyards than him! Especially now that his face was all blotched and his beard fallen out with his hair!

It is as well she kept these observations to herself, for if Richard had never yet asserted his marital rights or even the chaste kiss of a betrothed, he did regard his young wife as a possible enjoyment to come, should he ever be in condition to serve her as a husband.

All through that sweltering June and well into July the battle for Acre persisted. Meanwhile Richard, between renewed attacks of fever, insisted he be carried in a litter to direct both his and Philip's armies. He also received from Saladin, who had retired to Mount Carmel, gifts of fruit like those sent to his wife and sister, with courteous messages of concern for his illness.

Richard regarded these attentions as a sign that his enemy might be willing to discuss peace terms. He answered them with thanks for the fruit, and the enquiries after his health with an equally courteous request for a meeting if His Highness, the Sultan, would visit him in his tent. His fever, he assured Saladin, was not contagious.

But although Saladin sent him a polite reply that he would be only too willing to visit His Highness, 'The magnificent Coeur de Lion', as he grandiloquently named him, he added that 'kings should not have speech together until terms of a peace had been arranged.' Yet he agreed to a meeting between the 'Illustrious King of England' and his brother, Saphadin.

This Richard, still courteously polite, declined on plea of a further recurrence of his fever that necessitated a postponement of the meeting with His Highness, the Sultan's brother.

'I'll have naught to do with other than the Sultan himself,' he told Joan, 'for I mistrust the whole lot of them, and Saphadin, his brother, no less than any!'

Then, determined to woo Richard into acceptance of a peace treaty — which Richard thought might be a blind for more aggression — Saladin presented him with a further token of goodwill, the gift of a slave.

'As if you had not slaves enough without Saladin's blackamoor,' said Joan, who kept constant watch over her brother, soothing his hot forehead with a cloth soaked in snow. 'Another of his spies, I shouldn't wonder. There's more behind these friendly attentions than meets the eye!'

Which were also viewed with suspicion by the French, and noted by Joan, to her increasing anxiety since her own Muslim slaves had deserted to the Turks.

Richard, who had already signified his mistrust of the Sultan's brother if not the Sultan, ordered Berengaria to return to her ship with his sister. But Joan refused to leave him, and Berengaria also refused. Truth to tell, she rather enjoyed watching the battle from a safe vantage point and exchanging words, few of which she could understand, with the English soldiers who passed back and forth from the walls of Acre and the shore. One of these Crusaders she recognised as the young Scottish esquire who had been aboard her galley in the storm.

He was wounded, for blood-stained rags bound his forehead, bereft of his helmet while he worked with his fellows gathering driftwood on the shore to strengthen the barricades outside the encampment. She pointed to her forehead to enquire of his wound. He replied in his halting French, 'C'est rieng — nothing, Madame.' Their conversation was limited, for the most part, to signs since he knew no more of French than she of English, finding his Scottish accent almost incomprehensible. Yet this did not disguise the interest these two young people had in each other.

But on a day when there had been a temporary lull in the attacks of the Christians and fierce retaliation from the Muslims, the Scot, his arm now in a sling and limping as he walked, brought her news of the Duke of Burgundy who, fighting alongside the English, had captured several of the enemy, and also of the Count. He told her, 'So brave was the Count he cared not for his life...'

'The Count? What Count?'

'Of the French — of Flanders,' said the A'Hannach. 'He is killed — *mort* — dead.'

'No!' A hand leaped to her heart and all colour fled her face. 'Not my cousin — Philippe of Flanders?'

Without waiting for an answer she ran from him to her husband's tent, and was waylaid by Joan at the entrance. 'Sh!' with a hand to her lips. 'He sleeps. The fever is passing, thank God.'

'My cousin,' panted Berengaria, 'my cousin Philippe of Flanders — he is dead. Killed!'

Joan essayed to comfort her. 'Do not grieve for him, my dear. If, alas, it is the Count of Flanders who has been killed, he died a noble death in a good cause.'

'But I loved him,' sobbed Berengaria. 'He used to say we would be married when I grew up.'

Joan reminded her that the Count of Flanders already had a wife and a son whose name, she believed, was also Philippe. 'He is of an age to fight with the French, yet it is more likely to be the father of this young Count Philippe who has been killed. And now,' Joan said, 'go to the king, but go quietly. You must not disturb him.'

Greatly relieved, she did go quietly. Although sorry for Philippe, if his father had been killed she was more sorry for herself, since, she said miserably to herself, *I am married, so I could never have married Philippe, unless...* The thought crept in and was promptly crushed. She went on tiptoe to her husband's tent so as not to disturb him, but he was already disturbed by the sound of trumpets marshalling forces in the vicinity of the camp. He started up, threw off his bed coverings, and naked rushed to the door of the tent yelling for Ambroise, 'or one of you! Get me into my armour ... I go out!'

In vain did Joan try to hold him back, while Berengaria sneaked away giggling to see him in his nakedness — a great red hairy lion of a man. *I'd be terrified,* she told herself, *if he came at me as a husband or as a man should!*

Richard was still agitating for someone to get him into his armour, while Joan begged him to lie down. 'You'll get your death if you go out.'

'Philip,' he shouted, 'is attacking the walls. I forbade him to make another assault until we are sufficiently manned against Saladin's mamelukes. I sent a message to tell him this, but the swine will not heed me —'

Yet even as when armoured he made to leave the encampment, he collapsed and was carried back to his tent. There, fuming and raging against Philip, he lay, incessantly demanding reports of the latest developments. The French king's Crusaders were again repulsed, along with the Austrian and Pisan auxiliaries despite their valiant assaults on Saladin's camp to the north of Acre.

Philip then ordered a high wooden platform to be erected directly opposite the Accursed Tower, called by the French the 'Bad Neighbour'. From there he could continue to bombard the enemy with stones and rocks, but it was immediately destroyed by the Turks who had jocularly named it the 'Evil Kinsman'. Philip, in desperation, rebuilt the 'Bad Neighbour' only to see it fall again under the ceaseless attack of the Muslims.

Almost beside himself, with defeat gaining on him, Philip constructed a kind of scaling ladder which he called *'le Chat'*. Why he should have likened this rickety contrivance to a cat with which to pot at the Turks, only himself could know, but that again failed to subdue Saladin's aggressors. They set fire to a heap of dry wood, the flames of which seized the Cat and burnt it to cinders.

In his fury and mortification Philip ordered yet another fruitless attack upon Acre, which was the signal for more counter-charges against the Christians. But still the French, although aware that their king was likely to lose them the war unless the English king could leave his sick bed and come to their aid, 'displayed a fanatical courage', as reported by Borodin, one of Philip's eyewitnesses. 'Although met with savage resistance they held out in an implacable defence...'

One of the 'fanatics', an enormous Frenchman, stood on a parapet of the wall to launch great stones at the Muslims single-handed while riddled with the enemy's arrows. Undaunted, he kept his stance until the Muslims flung at him buckets of boiling oil and burnt him to ashes. The heroism of this giant won the grudging admiration of the Turks, and must have impressed Saladin with the indomitable spirit of the Christians, the son of whose God was their ally and even more of a powerful spirit than his own Mahomed. So much so that the Turks within the walls of Acre offered surrender if their lives and properties were spared.

Philip, in two minds whether to stay in or get out although Acre was still unconquered, received a message from Richard threatening that should he agree to surrender it would be to his peril. And on that very day the Marshal of France, encouraged by Richard's command and his vow to take Acre or perish, with a party of knights climbed a siege ladder to a breach in the wall near to the 'Accursed Tower'; but the ladder collapsed under the weight of the ascendants led by the Marshal. He fell and was instantly killed by a bowshot from the Turks.

Richard, weak from his illness, insisted he be brought on a stretcher to the scene of this last rally and, demanding a bow, he managed to shoot a Turk. Then, gaining strength, he offered a high reward to any who could dislodge a huge stone from the wall of the 'Accursed Tower'. Many volunteered but the operation caused numerous casualties and loss of lives. Nevertheless, so inspired by Richard were the French and English alike that both armies forced their way into the city against savage resistance from the Muslims. Yet again the Turks in the city offered to surrender, but Richard, still in command from his stretcher, shouted, 'Fools! Do you think I am such a weakling that I cannot take by force what you offer as a favour? See your shattered towers, your shaken walls, and then ask if I will accept the *gift* of a surrender before I can win this fight as victor! On with you to your master, the Sultan, and see if *he* will agree to a peace without one last bitter fight! He has more courage and determination than the whole lot of you. A worthy combatant!'

Saladin, as might have been expected, was as determined to hold the city as Richard to capture it. There were no more polite messages, gifts of fruit, flowers or negroes. While he waited for reinforcements from Egypt, whence an army of Muslims were now on the way to his headquarters, the Sultan ravaged the surrounding country, commanding his troops from his station on Mount Carmel. He gave orders that every Christian who opposed his army should be massacred, either by bowshot or hand-to-hand fighting or with their merciless scimitars and spears. On 8 July Haifa, where the Crusaders massed, was devastated with boiling oil and all Christians within the town burnt to death. Nor were the women and children who had accompanied their menfolk spared. Saladin then concentrated on cutting down the vineyards and orchards round Acre.

'Richard and Philip,' he told his brother Saphadin with grim satisfaction, 'will reap a harvest of ashes and festering corpses — if any are left from the feast of vultures — should the Lion Heart capture the city over my dead body, for only then will I capitulate.'

Said Saphadin, whom the Muslims called Voice and Echo since he never spoke more than his brother had spoken, and ever would repeat his words: 'Never over your dead body will the Christian kings capture our city. You are indestructible.'

And not even when the Accursed Tower collapsed with a roar of fallen stones and rubble did Saphadin waver in the belief of his brother's indestructibility as a disciple of Mahomed, with whose help Saladin, the All-Powerful, would conquer the Christians.

Yet Saphadin may have had cause to doubt his faith in the Will of Mahomed when Richard, recovered from his illness, gave command to 'that Brave and Noble Knight,' as Ambroise saw the Earl of Leicester who, assisted by the equally 'Brave and Noble Crusader' Hugh de Brun (later anglicised as Brown), and the warlike Bishop of Salisbury, to hack their way through the ruins of the city. Without realising they had adopted Saladin's orders to his infidels, they, with their long swords and spears, decapitated every Turk within reach of them, yelling, 'For Christ and the Holy Sepulchre!' Ruthlessly they chopped off legs and arms as they bore down upon helpless citizens, tradesmen, merchants, all sorts besides the fighting forces, regardless of the screams of women at the slaughter of their menfolk, or themselves if they got in the path of the Christian hordes bent on massacre.

But the Turks, indigenous to Acre and though starving after two years of siege, seized whatever weapons they could muster to aid the fighting forces against Leicester and his Crusaders, who were again repulsed. Even as they mounted the crumbling walls they were met with torrents of boiling pitch. Blazing streams of fire ran down the knights' armour, finding chinks in the joints and rivets so that many tore off their suits of mail, shrieking with the pain of their burnt bodies, and were killed by the deadly arrows of the Saracens. The deafening clash of steel, the very air stained red, with rags of flesh fluttering on the ends of spears or hooked on Turkish scimitars, might well have caused the stoutest heart to waver; yet none on either side gave up, and both Franks and English applauded the valour of the Infidel.

All through that desperate fighting, while Richard could take no active part in it, he gave orders from his tent to capture Acre in defiance of Philip's attempt to negotiate peace terms with Saladin. Richard would not hear of it, and only when the fighting on both sides had reached a deadlock did an assembly meet at the Templars' headquarters to discuss a possible agreement.

On Richard's insistence fifteen thousand bezants were to be paid each to himself and Philip; also fourteen hundred were to be paid to Conrad of Montferrat together with a hundred prisoners held by Saladin. This concession was urged by Philip in favour of Conrad, Lord of Tyre, who had deposed Guy de Lusignan as titular King of Jerusalem. No love was lost between Richard and Conrad, he having high-handedly refused to open the gates of Tyre when, after the sea fight against the Turkish ship sunk by Richard, fair winds had brought him and his victorious galleys to Conrad's port which was of supreme significance to the Third Crusade.

This undercurrent of hostilities between Richard and Conrad of Montferrat would bode no good to him of the Lion Heart.

Within the month allowed for the proposed agreement, the heralds made proclamations throughout the camp in praise of 'the famous Turks whom no man was to insult by word or deed ... Such valour and warlike excellence of men leaving the city almost penniless, struck wonder to the victors who gazed upon them whose loss failed to deject.' Prompted by Richard, these panegyrics were modified by the reminder that 'Only their superstitious rites and pitiful idolatry could rob these warriors of their strength.' If the English king had thought to sugar the bitter pill he offered Saladin with this eulogy of his 'famous Turks', it had the opposite effect.

Striding up and down his apartment in his fortress on Mount Carmel, the Sultan, attended by his brother Saphadin always in laudatory agreement with the All Highest, wheeled round upon Saphadin saying, 'Fetch me a scribe.'

A scribe, bowing — or rather crawling on all fours before the Presence — was bidden, 'Take this to the Christian Unbeliever.'

And 'this', dictated by Saladin expressing his disapproval of the 'Christian Unbeliever', was duly delivered to the effect that none of his Muslim banners must be removed from the Great Mosque of Islam.

It was received by Richard with hoots of laughter, echoed by his knights to cause another proclamation from the English king's heralds that all flags and banners bearing the sign of the Cross must fly from the walls and towers of the city.

Conrad, in an audacious move to assert his authority over that of the king, went one better. He ordered all banners of Islam to be torn down from the towers, minarets, and the Great Mosque, and that none but the Cross of the Crusaders should adorn the walls and towers of the city.

A black mark this, to be recorded against Conrad of Montferrat and not to be forgotten by the king…

The ultimate surrender of Acre was finalised a few weeks later. Richard had struck scarcely a blow for its capture since he had lain sick in his tent during the worst of the attack on the city.

Great were the rejoicings, with flags flying, bonfires blazing, trumpets blowing, and Richard receiving all glory to himself while Philip sulked. He had taken residence in the quarters of the Templars, but Leopold of Austria, heading a German contingent, who also had little to do with the capture of Acre, claimed equal conquest with the kings of France and England. He hoisted his standard beside that of Richard, but one of the knights — a Scot, the Stewart of Galloway — ripped it in half and flung it in a ditch. Then his esquire the A'Hannach took upon himself to attack three Turks single-handed, slicing them with his sword. They, taken by surprise and much stouter and older than the youngster, were no match for him. He managed to hurl all three of them into the mire, where they lay bleeding from the sword thrust of the sturdy Scot, and calling down the vengeance of Allah upon him and 'all uncircumcised dogs'.

This insult to his flag, which Leopold believed to have been at Richard's instigation, was destined to bring a bitter revenge from Austria to England's king.

In the palace of which Richard had taken possession with his wife and sister, feasting and roistering went on day in and night out. If at the height of his triumph Richard allowed the orgies of his knights, his sister Joan, always prudent and careful of her brother's young queen, removed her to the safety of their own apartments, much to Berengaria's dismay.

'I have a right to partner with the knights. Am I not Queen of England?'

'Yes, but we are not now in England,' Joan equably rejoined, 'we are in a country of barbarians and heathens, and it is not becoming to the Queen of England nor the Queen of Sicily as I am — or was,' she amended sadly, 'to participate in men's amusements, particularly when most of them are drunk.'

'Drinking,' pouted Berengaria, 'is accounted the privilege of knights, in especial when they celebrate a victory. My father often got a little drunk after a battle.'

Joan raised her eyebrows. 'I did not know your father was engaged in battles. Navarre has always been a peaceable country.'

'No! You know nothing of Navarre!' contradicted Berengaria, who of late — as Joan had noted with some apprehension — had shown signs of being less submissive than required of a seemingly docile princess to the authority of the king, her husband. And if, as Joan surmised, the girl though wife was still a virgin, how would she develop if wife other than in name? Richard, Joan believed, cared more for his military conquests than the conquest of women; and if rumour judged aright her brother preferred not only the society of men, but ... Conjecture paused. Never give thought to such discreditable gossip that savoured of blasphemy to the king of the Cross!

The ladies were not the only ones to leave the banqueting board. A young esquire who, if not the worse for drink, might have been emboldened by it to get up from his seat where the esquires of the knights were given place below the salt, to run into the centre of the hall. Here the rushes had been cleared for the convenience of the servers to wheel the heavy-laden trestles to the board and carve the roasted carcases of sheep or goats to be handed to the guests.

Numerous candles, lighting the platters of gold and silver on the board, reflected the flare of torches in their brackets on the walls to lend colours as of jewels, ruby, topaz, emerald amid the decorations of laurel and palm with the floral tokens laid before the kings of France and England. And in the space devoid of rushes on the stone floor, the young Scot, for it was he who had snatched a sword from a neighbour, and with his own weapon at his feet he began a wild dance between the two crossed swords.

'Hey, now!' cried Richard, 'what kind of caper is this? Never seen in Anjou nor in England, I'll warrant!'

'No, Sire,' was the answer from the Stewart of Galloway whose esquire had accompanied him from the court of William, King of Scots, the donor of vast sums for the Crusade. 'This is danced only in Scotland by a Scot, but he should be wearing the kilt and not cross-gartered hosen for the Fling.'

'He could scarce take on three Turks in a kilt, if that is what you call the knee-length skirt as worn by the Greeks in battle! Three against one on Acre's wall as I did see when you, Sir Knight, tore down the flag of Leopold of Austria — the German flag — and replaced it with our own, for which,' chuckled Richard, 'Leopold is unlikely to love us! And I saw, too, how this young Scot — what name is it?'

'Odo, the A'Hannach, Sire,' he was told.

'An outlandish name, but of uncommon courage. For he alone did tackle three Turks who came at him with their murderous scimitars as I saw when you threw the German flag into the ditch. And he, a mere lad and half their size, did seize them one by one, and while bleeding from a dozen wounds dragged them to the wall and kicked the arse of each and flung them in the mire to join the German flag. By God, 'twas laughable — I split my sides to see them sprawl there in the mud!'

And beckoning the youth, who had paused in his dance, he called to him, *Here! Come to me!* so Ambroise would have vouched for it. But even while he bowed before the king, a gash on the boy's beardless chin, where the blood had dried, broke open.

'You're hurt,' exclaimed Richard. 'You bleed.'

He drew himself up proudly. 'If, Sire, I bleed, 'tis for the honour of serving you and the Cross!' He spoke in his broad Scottish accent, but Richard interrupted with a boisterous demand to the assembled company.

'A sword — bring me a sword! He speaks as bold as he fights.'

A sword was brought while the Scot — in some alarm lest the king should think to smite him for speaking, as he thought, too 'bold'; and still in some doubt lest he had offended, understanding so little of the king's Norman French — knelt. Then Richard, with the sword, tapped the doubtless scared A'Hannach on the shoulder.

'Rise, Sir Odo, Knight of Scotland,' said the king.

He rose, and to the king's extended hand he bowed his lips. '*Per ardua ad alta,* by endeavour to the highest will I serve,' he said, 'the True Cross of the King.'

FIVE

In the first flush of victory Richard insisted that Philip and his Crusaders should remain in Jerusalem for at least three years, unless Saladin before that time should have surrendered his hold upon the Holy Land. Philip, however, who had been suffering from dysentery — or, more likely, jealousy of Richard for taking to himself all glory for the fall of Acre — told his knights, 'I have had enough of slaughter. I am weary of war.' (*And sick to death,* he might have added, *of Richard lording it over me as if he were the God Almighty for whom he is supposed to be fighting!*)

Ignoring the looks of horrified dismay from his knights at the thought that he, their king, would desert the Crusade, he continued, 'I will no longer sacrifice myself, my health and my Christians in the fight against the Infidel. He is stronger than all of us, incited as he is by Satan ... Go, tell Richard this, that I am done with the Crusade — and him!'

When Philip's emissaries, the Duke of Burgundy and the Bishop of Beauvais, came with this message to Richard, they could hardly deliver it for the shame they felt at Philip's desertion. Indeed, the old bishop's wrinkles held tears as Richard, interrupting their stammering recital, exclaimed, 'To hell with your king! If he leaves undone the Holy Mission to which he is pledged, he will bring everlasting contempt on himself and France. Go, tell him this — to do his damnedest! I'll have none of him and his works. May the devil take him whose vassal he is!'

Philip's desertion was keenly deplored by his nobles and knights; all believed that the only vindication for his dastardly purpose was to take his own life. Then, while recovering from his sickness — either physical or mental — he gave out that Richard had attempted to poison him. They all thought he was not far wrong in that assumption, and that Richard had taken his revenge upon Philip for so basely disgracing their Cause. His recovery, they declared, was due to the touch of a nail from the Cross.

How a nail from the Cross could have left the Sacred Tree to touch the King of France unless by a miracle, is unknown, but it sufficed to bring about a temporary truce between the two kings. Richard, awed by Philip's miraculous recovery from an illness of which he was reported to be dying, indicated that if the Saviour had pardoned him, Richard must follow Divine example. He therefore offered Philip a half share of all he had won to date during his Crusade, on condition he would continue to join forces with the King of England in his determination to capture the Holy City.

But Philip would not hear of it! He was adamant in his decision to return to France, being far too ill, he said, to continue in this appalling heat followed by swarms of flies and rats from the festering corpses that bestrewed their way to cause an epidemic of plague and death-dealing disease. 'I refuse,' whined Philip, 'to be one of those corpses!'

At which Richard inexcusably told him, 'Go then! And the sooner you *are* one of those corpses, the better for us!' Which did nothing to heal the breach in a trumped-up truce.

Philip departed in high dudgeon after Richard had insisted he must swear not to invade the lands and vineyards of Angevin … 'But I wouldn't count on his promise,' he told Joan, 'for all he agreed to "oblige" me. Hah! "Oblige" my arse for not grabbing what rightfully is mine! By God's Throat! Pity 'tis he wasn't poisoned, as he said, by what was given him to bring about his sickness. He's mad with jealousy of me for having achieved, while *I* lay sick, what he had failed to do who was here three months before I arrived! And he got nothing from his siege of the city but the loss of more than half his army. The sole reason for his return to France is to grab all he can get of the lands of Philip of Flanders, killed in the Battle of Acre, and which should rightly belong to me as Flanders joins Normandy and Philip of Flanders is — was — related to Navarre. Sancho had thought that the son of Flanders should wed her.'

'Maybe, until you, the better match, were arranged by our mother.'

'Navarre,' said Richard, 'hoped to have Flanders for himself or for Sancho, son of Navarre. But certain it is that Philip Augustus will never have Flanders.'

Nor did Philip Augustus have Flanders since he had more to do, for the present, in making peace if not with Richard with Guy de Lusignan and Conrad of Montferrat, both pleading their claim to the Crown of Jerusalem in a court over which the kings of France and England presided.

Neither could have appeared at their best. Richard had lost most of his hair, and his face was peeling and blotched with the aftermath of malaria, grandiloquently named by his doctors as 'leonardie', to which Philip had also succumbed, and was likewise a sorry sight and sorrier than any for himself.

The decision of the court finally agreed that Guy should hold the title of King of Jerusalem for life and that Conrad should succeed him.

All more or less thus amicably settled, with exception of Conrad who had an axe to grind against Richard and contemplated using it to intrigue with Saladin, and also to get his own back from Guy who he believed had, with Richard's connivance, usurped his right to the Crown of Jerusalem.

As for Philip, after granting his share of Acre to Conrad and affronting the Duke of Burgundy, a general in command of his army in Palestine, he sailed for Europe at the end of July. *He entrusted himself to the sea with tears and sobs and was carried by God's will to Apulia,* as one of the French chroniclers — Balion of Ibelin, who was hostile to Richard — had it. But despite his 'tears and sobs', presumably at leaving Acre, Philip was followed by the curses of the Crusaders and the blessings of Saladin who, welcoming so powerful and potential an ally, loaded him with gifts of attar of roses, rich clothes, dancing girls and every extravagant token of favour.

Conrad, equally anxious to get away from Acre and from Richard, took with him a number of Muslim prisoners of whom he thought to dispose on his own account as hostages; and last of all went Leopold of Austria, with more curses in his heart, not for Philip, but for Richard.

'And bloody good riddance of them all!' quoth Richard in equivalent Norman French.

Their departure left him in sole command of the Crusade, but the lesser chieftains, the German and Italian Crusaders so fiercely resented the supremacy of the English king that they would have set upon him with murderous intent had not the Templars intervened, forcing them to abandon their arms.

Richard, secure in the support of his Templars, ordered ships to be loaded with provisions for men and beasts, and that all Crusaders must prepare to follow him to Ascalon with their horses and military equipment, 'or,' he declared, 'to desert me and my army and earn the contempt of the whole Christian world, as have other — unmentionables!'

The Italian and German contingent, stung into submission by the English king's underlying threat but knowing he would not scruple to take drastic measures against them should they dare disobey his command, held themselves in readiness to follow where he led.

Meanwhile Saladin uneasily heard from Richard's envoys the decision of the Council that he was ordered to pay monthly instalments of a ransom for the restoration of the Holy Cross held by the Sultan's Muslims, with some sixteen hundred prisoners, and that Conrad must return to Acre with all the prisoners in his custody.

Conrad's reply to Richard's demand was a flat refusal to return to Acre, with or without his prisoners. According to Ambroise (who seemed to have ears for news that came to him borne of the winds or conveyed by some mystic or deific source), Conrad had amplified his refusal with the defiant assertion that he would never meet Richard again for he feared him more than any man alive.

'This is madness!' roared Richard. 'That he should fear me he has reason, but to dare hold back his prisoners from me is sheer lunacy and he'll regret it! I'll go myself and fetch his Muslims…'

And only at the advice of the more prudent Templars that Conrad, already proved to be a potent danger, could withhold all supplies to Acre and further delay the departure for Ascalon, did Richard see the sense of this. He then sent Philip's representative, the Duke of Burgundy, to remonstrate with Conrad, who reluctantly agreed to give up his prisoners but still refused to be reconciled to his king.

Richard believed that Conrad in his persistent defiance must be in league with Saladin, particularly as the Sultan insisted that all Muslim prisoners held by the Franks, including Conrad's hundreds, should be released in exchange for the garrison of Acre. This being out of the question, Richard was roused to furious retort that if Saladin did not agree to a compromise, to free all Christian prisoners in return for the release of imprisoned Muslims, when the monthly instalments of payment should be paid in full, he would...

The unfinished threat left no doubt in Saladin's mind that the lives of the prisoners in the garrison at Acre were forfeit, and still he stubbornly rejected agreement to Richard's terms. Rumour gave it that sooner than accede to the English king's demands, Saladin had killed his own imprisoned Muslims. An unlikely assumption that did, however, spur Richard to immediate action.

'So be it!' he commanded. 'Bring forth the survivors of Saladin's murders, that we may know who are and who are not worthy of sacrifice!'

On 20 August Richard, believing that Saladin, sooner than render up his Christian prisoners in exchange for Muslims, would annihilate all those held in the garrison at Acre, decided on a drastic alternative. There were at least two and a half thousand Muslims in custody at Acre, and of these not all were prisoners but innocent citizens. Richard ordered that every one of them — men, women and children — should be bound in chains and slaughtered.

Of the many atrocities committed on both sides by Saracens and Christians alike in the name of the Prophet and the name of God, this was perhaps the most barbarous, and Richard has borne the stain of it throughout both the Christian and the Unbelieving world. Yet there were some of Richard's time to whom the lives of the Unbelievers were of no account since they were doomed to hell in any case. And, as Saint Bernard of

Clairvaux gave it, 'The Christian glories in the death of a pagan, because thereby Christ himself is glorified.'

Poor comfort this to Richard when he saw, and with what miserable penitence, his massacre of innocents. *But,* he muttered within him, *my Crusaders have only obeyed my command who obey the word of God...*

Watching from the plain between the two hills that divided the Christian and Saracen camps, Richard, having given the order for the butchery of the Muslims — after sorting out the more important prisoners to be spared for ransom or held as slaves — was agonised to see children and infants torn from their shrieking mothers' arms to be mercilessly slain.

When the bodies of the male corpses were ripped open a quantity of gold and jewels were found in the entrails of the wealthiest, who had obviously swallowed them to be vomited if their lives were spared. Yet none among the Christians raised hand or voice in protest against these brutal murders. And thereafter in many Christian cities as of Burgundy or Anjou could be seen frescoes depicting savage beasts, lions and dragons, tearing their victims limb from limb, while Knight Templars stood by applauding the Will of God as given in the contemporary chronicles of the *Romance de Richard Cuer* (sic) *de Lyon:*

'Seynors, tuez, tuez!
Spare hem nought, behideth these!
King Richard herd the Angelus voys
And thankyd God and the Holy Cros...'

When the Saracens saw the massacres not only of the Muslim prisoners but of their women and children, they swarmed into the very midst of the slaughter, hot for vengeance; but even as they fought all that day and night they failed to break through the strong armoured defence of the Crusaders, and were compelled to retreat leaving the plain beneath the garrison strewn with the bodies of Saracens as well as those of mutilated prisoners.

Saladin, having conceded to Richard his demand for the release of all Christians he still held in custody, saw with horror the butchery of innocent women and children as well as the inoffensive citizens of Acre. He at once took reprisals. His army descended on the Christian camp, hanging and disembowelling the many who could not escape; yet the more important who had held the garrison he ordered to be sold in his slave markets; the money thus obtained would be distributed among his troops.

But Richard, still the conqueror of Acre, thought it advisable to send his two queens in advance of his departure for Ascalon. Although the palace where they lodged was well guarded, he guessed that Saladin would not scruple to attempt further reprisals and seize the two women as hostages, also the child of Isaac Comnenus of Cyprus, and hold all three of them for ransom.

So Joan and Berengaria with their attendants, and Isaac's little daughter and her nurse, followed by galleys laden with provisions, awaited the order for their departure. Berengaria was loth to leave the safety of the palace for a hazardous journey by sea or land, and heaven alone knew what disasters might befall them from savage, merciless Saracens. Nor was she at all pleased with the prospect of renouncing the delights of the conquered city, which had offered bountiful entertainments, as Ambroise gave it, of *Good wines and beautiful girls to which the men abandoned themselves with all manner of follies.*

It is unlikely that Berengaria partook of 'all manner of follies' with sister Joan ever watchful beside her, but she doubtless sampled her share of the 'good wines', which no longer had upon her the disastrous effect she suffered at her wedding feast. But Joan, urged by Berengaria, prevailed upon her brother to delay their departure from Acre rather than endure the misery of a journey to Ascalon in the sweltering heat of the summer. He therefore agreed to delay until the cooler weather of the autumn.

Reluctantly did Richard's Crusaders prepare to leave the pleasures of Acre, as recorded by Saladin's secretary Imad-ad-Din, who has given much authentic detail of the Saracen offensive against the Pilgrims, and described the women who offered themselves for the enjoyment of the Christian troops as:

Tinted and painted, desirable and desirous...
bold and ardent with fleshy thighs ... They
interwove leg with leg, themselves targets
for men's darts, and maintained this as an
act of piety without equal to those who were
far from home and wives ...

Such acts, in which Richard's knights and men were thus delighting, may have hastened his departure. He mustered his army again with strict orders that none but the washerwomen, who would not offer tempting 'acts of piety' to Christ's soldiers, were permitted to follow the camps, and so with his Crusaders he left Acre.

Since the Mecca of his pilgrimage was Jerusalem, Richard knew that to go direct from Acre not only across barren desert but over hilly land in this blazing summer would have been murder for his troops in their weighty armour. He therefore decided to make for Jaffa, marching south along the coastline, thence to the Holy City.

Leaving instructions for his womenfolk to join him so soon as he could find for them adequate accommodation, and after the rainfalls when the weather should have cooled, he departed from Acre with hope in his heart that at last he would reach his goal.

Richard suffered much criticism for his absorption in this, the third Crusade to the neglect of his country and of which his brother John, Count Mortain, was not slow to take advantage.

When his mother, Queen Eleanor, had met Richard, with Berengaria offered as an alternative bride to the jilted Alais of France, the Queen Mother warned Richard of her suspicions concerning her youngest son, John. 'Although I say it of him I bore to your father, and —'

'Who,' Richard with smiling haste interrupted, 'cast doubts that I am his father's son. He frequently alludes to the colour of my hair which, unlike any one of us, is red as a fox, and I as cunning.'

'Your brother,' Eleanor had reminded him, 'has seen himself King of England and Duke of Normandy ever since your father breathed his last, with curses on him whom he had loved beyond all knowledge of his treachery. As for your colour, you throw back to your Norman forbears. They called the only surviving son of William of Normandy "Red Rufus". William was the second conqueror of England, the first being Caesar of Rome.'

'Never again,' swore Richard, flaming, 'by God's Throat will England be conquered, though many will make the attempt, but none shall succeed in my reign nor in all future reigns to come.'

'Yes,' agreed his mother, 'so long as you can withhold your brother John from making the attempt. France, or Philip Augustus of that country divided from yours by a narrow strip of water, has cast covetous eyes on your island of fog — God knows why, for 'tis a land fit only for the naked savages with their flesh painted blue as once these Angles were, and it is to their undoing that they ever emerged from their savagery.'

'How you dislike my kingdom,' smiled Richard, 'as always you disliked my father.'

'Not always. I was infatuated with him — a likely lad with his blond hair and handsome looks and a charm to melt stones or all women — even I, twelve years his elder. *Mais revenons a nos moutons* — or to my bleating lamb, John...'

The Queen's warning went unheeded, and not until some eighteen months after the fall of Acre did Richard learn how John had been stirring up trouble against Longchamp.

Richard had appointed Longchamp chief justiciar, which, in Plantagenet times, was tantamount to a regency, in that he stood as head of the state in the absence of the king. John, in common with the majority of the king's subjects, resented the rise to power of this detested 'monster of arrogance', as he was known to both clergy and laymen.

A contemporary description of him by Gerald of Wales gives an unforgettable picture of the man who had risen to the height of authority by reason of the king's favour and trust in him; and despite his lack of physical attraction, he could be a worthy diplomat and shrewd politician as head of the realm. There were few of Richard's subjects, either clerical or secular, who shared the king's faith in him. He was utterly unscrupulous and, as generally accepted, a sexual pervert. This, however, would not have disfavoured him in the eyes of Richard; but it served to increase John's hostility to the one who not only ruled his brother's kingdom but showed marked dislike of the heir presumptive, as John wishfully thought himself to be.

The description we have of William Longchamp's appearance in addition to his character for greed, cupidity, and inordinate ambition, is:

...of a contemptible stature, crippled in both haunches, with a big head and hair coming almost to his eyebrows like an ape's ... His neck was short, his back humped, and his belly stuck out in front and his buttocks at the back...

In fact he had everything in his disfavour for John to use as a weapon against him who made no attempt to disguise his hatred of the England he served. Longchamp brought over a troupe of French minstrels and jugglers from France and taught them to sing his praises in a couplet to be bawled in London's streets.

You do such great things so easily and well
But whether you are good or bad no man can tell.

The last line of this had been freely translated by John to suit the mood of Londoners. He had further cause to resent and fear so dangerous a rival as William Longchamp when the Chancellor seized control of the castles and domains that Richard had conferred upon his brother; and so still more did he mistrust this 'upstart usurper of my rights', as he called him.

(*And my throne,* he inly added, convinced that Richard would never survive his perilous Crusade.)

When John learned that Longchamp was making a secret treaty with William, King of Scots concerning the succession of Prince Arthur in the event of Richard's death, his fear of this Longchamp knew no bounds.

In the November of the previous year (1190) Richard had named his nephew Arthur as his heir. And Longchamp, having learned of the treaty with Tancred of Sicily that Arthur should marry Tancred's daughter when both should reach marriageable age, at once sent ambassadors to Tancred confirming the king's decision.

Now began the inevitable conflict between John and William Longchamp who, John realised, would be a powerful menace to his future prospects unless he could bring about the downfall of the loathly Chancellor.

It was Hubert Walter, Bishop of Salisbury, who had accompanied Richard at the start of his Crusade and stayed with him until after the fall of Acre; and he succeeded where the Queen Mother had failed in warning the king of his brother's treachery.

Unlike the majority of the other bishops, Hubert Walter was less a man of the mitre than a man of the world. Richard admired and respected Hubert, who cared for the Crusaders as much for their bodies as for their souls. With a watching brief, as it were, in the Middle East, Hubert of Salisbury had learned of the trouble John was brewing in England so soon as the king had left his kingdom to the care of the Chancellor. With tactful emphasis did the Bishop of Salisbury impart his information to the king.

'It has come to my knowledge that Your Grace's brother, Prince John, Count of Mortain, has been in league with Philip,

King of France, ever since the French king deserted the Crusade and returned to his own country. Prince John,' said the bishop, his eyes on the ceiling, his hand worrying his chin between two fingers, 'has been approached by King Philip with a bait — if I may so suggest it — that the prince, your brother, Sire, shall marry the Princess Alais with the promise that all the lands assigned to Your Grace on the French side of the English Channel — Anjou and Normandy — and whatever the King of England holds in France, shall be given to Prince John on his marriage.'

At this astounding pronouncement, suavely presented, Richard flared in irate denial.

'This preposterous — unthinkable and ridiculous — if I may dare oppose your lordship's suggestion which has come to you — God knows how — all these hundreds or thousands of miles, unless by carrier pigeon.'

'The proverbial little bird?' the bishop smilingly intervened.

'Little bird or vulture's chicken,' shouted Richard, 'ready to prey on my carcass! Philip hates my guts, though he once professed his love for me even to the sharing of my bed —'

The bishop's hand left his chin to lift it in admonishment. 'None pays heed to such malicious slander, Sire.'

'My father did, and as for John — he loved and trusted him above all of us, both his bastards by Rosamond and his sons by our mother. John is weak and ambitious, I grant you, and looked upon himself as my successor after the death of my two brothers. Yet I am convinced he would never seek to injure me by word or deed. As for marrying Alais, surely you must know that such a marriage is impossible. He has a wife already.'

'Which,' said the bishop, smiling, 'would not, I think, trouble Count Mortain, nor the King of France, who is bent on avenging or righting what he believes to be the wrong that you, as King of England, has done to his sister, the Princess Alais — to deprive her, to whom you were betrothed, of her queenship as your consort.'

'Never,' denied Richard loudly, 'by *my* will was I betrothed to Alais. I knew her to be my father's mistress and that she had borne him a child — a girl, I understand. As for Philip, I can deal with him so soon as I have completed my mission to the Holy Land, to which I am dedicated. May I and my kingdom perish before I will desert my Cause!'

'Your Grace,' the bishop persevered, 'will permit me to return, for the meantime, to England. I can better serve you there than here where I am so far removed from any mischief from the grievance of your fellow Crusader, the King of France —'

'You allow too much credit to your news carrier's pickings from the garbage of Philip's court, which is of no more account than the droppings of sparrows,' snarled Richard.

'Or those of a vulture's chickens?' he was mildly reminded. 'But without destroying your faith in and brotherly love for Count John and your friendship with King Philip, I again ask leave of Your Grace that I return to England as soon as may be.'

'Are you determined to desert me and my mission as Philip has done?' demanded Richard.

'Sire.' The bishop approached him to lay a hand on his shoulder. 'My son — never in my life nor death would I desert you and your kingship, for believe me I act solely in your interest and that of your kingdom.'

'Well,' a deep sigh preceded the words, 'I abide by your judgement, yet only on condition that you return to me when I have completed what I intend to do — the deliverance of the

Holy City from the accursed Unbeliever, so that I may receive your blessing at the foot of our Saviour's Cross...'

Richard was not to be delayed from the mission to which since his boyhood he had been dedicated by the croakings, as he told himself, of an over-zealous bishop. From the outset of his venture Hubert Walter had endeavoured to dissuade him from the neglect of his throne. 'As God's Anointed', he would often urge him, 'your first duty is to your kingdom.'

On the day of the bishop's departure with his retinue of servants, his chaplain, horses, camels, and two galleys laden, at Richard's insistence, with provisions, the king again set out upon his march.

The bulk of the army, totalling about a hundred thousand in three columns of infantry including the mounted archers led by Richard, advanced along the coastal road southward to Jaffa. It was hard going on that rough track through dry bush flanked by the burning white sand of the shore in the torrid subtropical heat that showed no sign of abating.

The two queens, Joan and Berengaria, left behind under strict surveillance in the deserted palace at Acre, had no news of the Crusaders' march, since messengers could not be spared: every man would be needed in what Richard knew must be severe fighting with Saladin's troops. They, accustomed to the blazing August heat, would be in better case to combat the Christians in their heavy coats of mail. Nor was the king at all anxious to have ill news brought to his women, who had rebelled against being left in the fallen city among conquered Saracens — 'and savages, however grateful they may appear for not being butchered by you!' Berengaria sulkily told her husband. 'They have no love for us, and if they could, they would do to *us* what you have done to them.'

She was full of complaints to Joan, ever bewailing her fate in having been 'forced to marry a man who admits he is old enough to be my father and cares for — in fact *loves* the horse he took from that odious Isaac in Sicily more than ever he cared for me! I ought never,' she whimpered, 'have agreed to such a marriage and to a man who has never given me more than a kiss on my cheek for good morning or good night. And never has he come to my bed. Not that I'd want him to — the thought of what I would have to endure if he — if he did with me as a husband does with his wife...' She shuddered. 'I ... I'd *hate* it, and him!'

To which Joan, at a loss how to counter this startling admission, achieved, unconvincingly, 'Richard has too much love for you to enforce his marital rights until you are willing to accept them. Besides, he feels that you are safer in my care than to follow the Crusade and all its hardships, which are unfit for any woman, much less so young a girl...'

'I would *want* to suffer hardships!' retorted Berengaria, 'and is it my fault I am a girl? Not so young neither, at all but eighteen. I was meant to be a boy, so my father often told me. My mother didn't want a girl — she didn't like girls, and anyhow I was a mistake. She tried not to have any more children. It can be prevented. My old nurse, who had been my mother's nurse, told me of something — before I was to be married — that I could do to prevent it. As for me, I'll never have a child, Richard being disinclined to get me one. So I am saddled with Isaac's brat to bring her safely back to Cyprus — if ever this Crusade is done with, and that, so far as I can see, will be *never!*

Joan, although mildly remonstrant with the rebellious Berengaria's complaints, could not but inwardly agree that she had some cause to rebel. Joan, who had been used to the homage of her husband's subjects, and had queened it regally in Sicily, could no more adapt herself to the discomfort of following her brother's foolhardy fanatical Crusade — as she dared to name it — than did Berengaria.

'But,' she pacifically attempted, 'we are better off here in the care of these guards than if we were sent back to England to face the perils of the sea as we did on our way out.'

'We will have to face it on our way in if we are ever to get out of here,' was Berengaria's reply. 'I'm sick to death of having to follow the army — and not so much do I get from it as were I a camp-following whore.'

'For shame!' uttered the scandalised Joan; thinking, *She may be nothing so simple as Richard would have us believe...* And she wondered if the name 'Damozel' bestowed on the Princess of Navarre, 'presumably a virgin', had been a misnomer.

Meanwhile Richard, regardless of the heat affecting him and his infantry in their heavy armour, rode at the head of his column, mounted on the stallion Fauvel, captured from Isaac Comnenus in the conquest of Cyprus. Beside him rode Ambroise who, dividing his attention between his tablets and his mettlesome horse, was loud in his praise of 'the fairest company and most valiant and choicest ever seen!'

At the foot of a range of hills where Saladin kept ceaseless watch, the columns halted to strike camp for the night. But scarcely had they raised a tent for the king than the Sultan gave the order for attack. About forty or more Saracen horsemen descended on the 'fairest company', who had reluctantly been torn away from the fairer company of women at Acre and, taken by surprise, were given little time hastily to don their armour before the Turkish horsemen, flourishing their scimitars, and the deadly poison-tipped arrows were upon them.

The English and Norman knights, organised in three divisions, were protected from the Sultan's galleys attacking on the coastal side by the foot soldiers. Those under attack from the advancing Turks saw that many of the knights chased the Saracen horsemen looking *like a cavalry of porcupines with arrows stuck in them*, as the irrepressible Ambroise reported.

The first rose fingers of dawn caressed the sky when, after a severe hammering, the Turks were forced to retreat. Ambroise, gleefully scribbling, described the rout of the enemy: *Screaming in their high-pitched voices, there is no god but Allah* — who seemed, however, to have let them down.

And now with Saladin's armies licking their wounds preparatory to a further offensive, Richard, despite that all were exhausted with the night's activities and no rest, decided to toil on in the cool of early morning before the heat of high noon.

Over the ridge of Mount Carmel where Saladin, having witnessed the retreat of his horsemen, sent a swarm of his Turks — 'like locusts,' said Ambroise — razing to the ground fortresses and crops to impede Richard's armies who were steadily making for Caesarea past Haifa.

The heat from a brassy unclouded sky claimed many victims of sunstroke, while all along the route over that rough-hewn way the army doggedly marched though many fell by the wayside. No time was allowed for burial of Richard's 'fairest and choicest', whose corpses lay on the sandy bush to be devoured by expectant vultures. Yet never would the Servants of the Cross surrender to the rain of Turkish arrows.

A march of two days brought them to Haifa, and on the outskirts of the town they pitched their tents. It was evident the Saracens had been there before them, for the ground was down-trodden and the refuse of food and bones, not all devoured by prowling pariah dogs and predators, were scattered and stinking to high heaven. The wounded were cared for by the washerwomen and the officers' servants. William de Barres, the French knight with whom Richard had fallen out some months earlier over the trifling matter of the reed canes, was now taken back into favour for having distinguished himself for valour when the Saracens had swooped down upon the vanguard led by Richard. A'Hannach, the Scot, whom Richard had knighted in one of his impulsive gestures for disposing of three Turks single-handed on the walls of Acre, had again fought a stout Turk twice his size when, although severely wounded in his right hand, he had seized the Turk's deadly scimitar and turned it on him to cut his throat.

After a night's rest and the quenching of their thirst at a welcome spring, the march was resumed with more difficult going over that devastated ground where Saladin's troops had preceded them; but the foot soldiers fared the worst. They had to hack their way through thorn and scrub, sick and weary as they were, while the mounted knights were much better off on their good horses that could trample down bush and thick reeds at the foot of the mountains and deal with attack from tarantulas that had founded colonies all along their path.

Another march of eight miles brought them to Caphernaum, and here again Saladin had left the debris of his camp. They stopped there for a hasty meal, and after a further four miles they came to Casal (the village) of the Straits. Here they spent two days and, followed along the coast by the fleet, were able to unload fresh supplies from the galleys. They dared not delay longer, for they knew that Saladin awaited their arrival with a formidable offensive on a grander scale than any that had gone before.

The Muslims, accustomed to the climatic conditions, were in far better case to fight — and, as Saladin hoped, finally to annihilate once and for all — the Christian 'uncircumcised dogs'.

The Crusaders were less fit to deal with the Turks, since many of the wounded had been taken aboard the following galleys unfit for active service. Others able to limp — or, if mounted, to ride — had to contend not only with tarantulas but also wild beasts. The Hannay (A'Hannach), despite his right hand, had been almost sliced in half by the Turk he had killed in self-defence, managed left-handed to spear a bear that when skinned and roasted provided a feast round the camp fires; for while the days were insufferably hot, the nights were cool after the blistering sun.

During the thirty-six hours passed at Casal all the knights, before they took to their hastily contrived beds, stretched their arms in prayer and thankfulness for their deliverance, thus far, from the enemy, and sent up a chorus of *Sanctum Sepulchrum Adjuva* ('Help us, O Holy Sepulchre'). But so soon as they laid their heads to rest, swarms of tarantulas were at them again, and sleep fled before the incessant clash of helmets, armour, spears, shields, pots and pans to drive off the intruders.

'Worse than an army of infidels,' groaned Richard, who had saved himself a bite from one of the huge hairy brutes by grinding it to pulp with his battle axe, and retched up his heart at sight of the bloody mess. 'I'd liefer pound an Infidel's flesh to jelly than this!' said he; and little rest did any of them have that night.

Their next halt was Caesarea, and Richard, on each stage of the journey to the Holy City, was reminded of places where the Saviour had travelled more than a thousand years before. The army camped on the banks of the River of Crocodiles, so named for two knights who, on an earlier crusade, had been eaten alive there by crocodiles. This, however, did not prevent Richard from stripping off his armour and plunging into the blessedly cool water. Some of the knights followed suit, and here, too, a ship with more supplies had come. But the columns led by Richard were not allowed time for further dalliance, they must pursue their way through the burning sand dunes along the shore toward Jerusalem. And here they were met by a dozen or more mounted Saracens who pelted them with arrows but were speedily put to flight by the bolts from the foot soldiers' cross-bows. Richard, dismounting from his stallion Fauvel, brandished his deadly battle axe and, dashing in among the Muslim cavalry, sent them galloping off. The king received an arrow in his side that pierced his coat of mail, yet the injury was slight. He pulled it out, staunched the flow of blood and remounted, making light of his hurt to the anxious Ambroise. 'It is not poisoned, or I'd not be up here,' said he, 'but down there.' He pointed below to a pile of brushwood that the mounted Muslims had demolished.

The way along the shore had now become impassable owing to the heavy vegetation and tall papyrus reeds on the mountain slopes down to the rough track beside the sea that retained traces of a Roman road. Even the horses could not force a path through an almost impenetrable jungle fringing the shore, so Richard ordered them to make their way inland.

But Saladin had no mind to risk an engagement with the enemy until he had moved his Turks south into the Forest of Arsüf for cover, leaving enough of his cavalry to harass the Christians, wearied with their long march of many days in the August heat and so weak from their wounds and sunstroke that some thought to give up and die. Yet Richard cheered them on by commanding litters to be cut from branches, as there were not enough stretchers left to carry them.

'I know,' he said, 'that you would fight to the last drops of your blood, but rather than leave you here to be devoured by wild beasts — there are lions about these parts, if one can believe that Daniel of the lions' den lived around here in olden times — I would sooner you fell in fight against the Saracens.'

Richard was generous in his praise of the Muslims no less than he admired Saladin for his superb generalship. And like Richard, the Sultan fought his battles in person. He would ride in the midst of an attack fearlessly disregardful of danger from the arrows or spears of the Christian knights or of Richard's fearsome battle axe.

On learning that Richard had been wounded by an arrow, Saladin at once sent to know if he could supply him with a soothing ointment of which he had the recipe from one of his physicians.

Both warriors had a mutual respect for the other. Of Richard, Saladin was reported to have said that if he had to lose Jerusalem he would rather lose it to Malek Ric (Richard) than to any other prince in or out of Christendom.

Yet even while he doggedly pushed on with his depleted army, Richard had to face and counter-charge attacks from the Saracens under the command of Saladin, as determined to conquer the Crusaders as was Richard to serve the Cross.

Richard now realised that a battle fiercer than any that had gone before was imminent, and he was also aware of the danger to his army from Saladin's superior forces, which had not suffered so desperately as had his troops from heat, shortage of rations, sickness and fatal casualties.

At nightfall on the last day of August the enemy withdrew for a breathing space after their incessant bombardment from the Templars' cavalry. Richard was encamped some eight miles from Caesarea, almost in sight of the enemy, while Saladin had moved on up the River of the Dead, so called for its sluggish flow between thickly matted reeds and rushes.

There was little here to restore the king's wearied men. Of the rations brought from the galleys, much had become inedible owing to the scorching heat that struck down many of the mules and even the camels carrying sacks of provisions. Also some of the cavalry's horses had died from their wounds and their flesh seized and eaten raw by the ravenous men. Even the knights had come to blows with each other for a share of the meat, so starving were they, until Richard roared at them, 'What! Will you fight among yourselves for the bodies of our horses who have so faithfully served and died for us? Are you cannibals? Eat grass or chew the cud and slake your thirst at the spring!'

Sheepishly they gave in and sucked at the stems of the papyrus reeds until, exhausted and empty though they were of food, they managed to get some sleep.

Meanwhile Saladin was assembling his forces for a final attack against the 'uncircumcised Christians', which he vowed would be their end; yet, as he gave it to his scribe and chronicler Bohardin, he regretted he must bring about the downfall of *so valiant an adversary as the English Lion Heart.*

Richard chose from among his knights one Humphrey of Toro who, adopting a disguise and could speak and understand a modicum of Arabic, had sneaked into the Saracen camp and reported to Richard not only the Sultan's good opinion of him but a resumé of his planned offensive. This gave Richard to consider a parley with Saladin in order to gain time for more reinforcements coming from the coast at Acre, where the following fleet had landed them. He also knew from

Humphrey's snooping, disguised as a vendor of fruit in baskets fashioned from reeds, that the Sultan would not be averse to a parley since he, as did Richard, awaited strong reinforcements.

'So,' Richard grimly commented, 'it is for us to see which one will get in first!'

Back again went Humphrey, no longer a whining mendicant but a Knight Templar mounted on his charger with his surtout over a coat of mail and bearing a shield emblazoned with the white Cross; and with him went Richard on Fauvel, regally attired, his shield carrying the royal insignia of the golden leopards.

They were met by Malek-el-Adil, the Sultan's brother Saphadin. courteous bows were exchanged in the tent set aside for the interview, and a sticky sweetmeat offered with sherbet. Richard had hoped for wine.

'What conditions,' the king was asked, with profound grandiloquence, 'does your Excellency the Lion Heart, second only to the All Highest, my esteemed brother, Chosen of Allah, propose to suggest in your name to Salah-ed-Din, the All Highest Sultan of Egypt and Syria?'

'Our conditions,' replied Richard, exchanging a glance with his knight interpreter, 'we hope may please the All Highest, whom we hold in the greatest esteem.'

More bows from Saphadin, and a signal to a slave bearing dishes of a sticky jelly-like sweetmeat, later known in England as Turkish Delight; and a replenishment of Richard's goblet of sherbet that cause the Lion Heart a fit of the hiccups, and to say, when sufficiently recovered from the revolting fizzy stuff, 'If I may suggest — *hic* — pardon me — to the All Highest the one and *only* condition is, that the whole of Palestine now held by the Chosen of Allah —' another gratified bow from Saphadin, who was unprepared for what came next — 'be restored to the servants of Christ, and not —' as interpreted by Humphrey — '*one* single part of it, but the *whole* of our Holy Land. Failing which,' Richard paused to extract with an exploratory finger a morsel of the sickly-sweet jelly, 'I shall reluctantly — *hic* — be compelled to demand that your brother, the All Highest, return — where he belongs.'

As Saphadin understood enough of Sir Humphrey's rendering of Richard's ultimatum abruptly to conclude negotiations, he now, with the smallest of bows, gestured the guards at the entrance of the tents to conduct the visitors thence.

'So that — is that!' remarked Richard as he mounted Fauvel and rode off beside Humphrey. 'And here are we, all ready for the fray to decide which of us is the chosen of our Lord Christ or their Lord Allah to regain the Holy Sepulchre — and be damned if this filthy thing he served me don't pull out a tooth!'

It was evident that Saladin had decided to make for a plain north of the Forest of Arsüf still bordered with woods thick enough to provide shelter for his cavalry. But Richard's army, no longer to be held back awaiting reinforcements from Acre, marched on leading the Normans and English in charge of the Royal Standard. He divided five battalions into two squadrons, horse and foot, with the Duke of Burgundy and some of his picked knights in command. He had ordered his army to fight its way through Arsüf along the seashore.

It was now the first of September, and Richard hoped to delay the final and victorious engagement until the heat of summer had passed. But as the Christian army neared Arsüf, skirting the forest, a great wave of Negro and Bedouin foot soldiers bore down upon the vanguard, yelling and howling their native war cries while they showered their arrows and darts at the foremost mounted knights amid clouds of dust kicked up by the horses' hooves. *But we put to flight,* as Ambroise triumphantly records it, *the black-faced heathens!* whose intent, as they retreated under Saladin's orders (again we have it from Ambroise) *was to set fire to the Forest of Arsüf and make so great a burning to roast all of us alive as we marched in...*

Heedless of this dire threat, Richard, knowing Ambroise to be possessed of a vivid imagination with which he embroidered his accounts of the Crusade, rode on at the head of his army, avoiding the forest that showed no sign of burning. He guessed that the attack of the 'black-faced heathens' had been Saladin's attempt to create confusion among the vanguard of the Templars, while the Turkish cavalry, in renewed strength, came at the rearguard of the Christian foot soldiers — *swifter than eagles,* as reported by Ambroise from his safe vantage point behind the lines:

They thundered down upon us amid whirling dust that darkened the air to the accompaniment of a horrid din of drums, brass gongs, rattles and screams of 'There is no god but Allah and his prophet Mahomed'...

Yet it was evident, despite the unfailing courage of the knights and foot soldiers who in the rear had come to the aid of the Templars and Hospitallers, that the battle must be won by the Turks unless the king's men could take the offensive.

All through the blistering heat of that first September day, the casualties among the knights were only outnumbered by those of the gallant foot soldiers who, marching backward, refused to retreat and sent bolts from their crossbows at the oncoming Turkish cavalry, striking down the foremost with deadly aim. The choking dust, whirling around that melee of men and horse; the incessant clash of steel in a multitudinous frenzy of sight and sound, the shriek of wounded horses, the groans of the dying, the very air blood-stained, and rags of flesh alighting on the tips of spears and scimitars like gigantic scarlet butterflies; the continuous roar of the Muslims in a united chorus of 'Allah, Allah-oohah!' amid the thunder of horses' hooves, resembled a mighty tidal wave from a submarine eruption.

Many of the knights whose horses had been killed under them were fighting hand-to-hand with the emirs, who hammered at the Templars with their maces and murderous scimitars, themselves unhorsed and dripping blood from their sliced arms and legs. They, unlike the Christians, were not armoured head to foot, and their knee-length tunics gave less protection to their lower limbs that, although encased in mail, were vulnerable to the razor-sharp edge of swords and lances.

But the Muslim army had the advantage of being impervious to the heat; born to it, they could withstand the sweltering effects of the sun while in that grim deadlock neither side would give way. The discipline of both Christians and the 'black-faced heathens' despised by Ambroise, remained impeccable.

There was, however, some impatience among the Crusaders at the long delay of the king in taking the offensive against Saladin's main force. Richard, however, knowing that his troops would be unable to deal with the superior Muslim ranks, insisted on holding back the offensive until further reinforcements from Acre arrived. In vain did Garnier de Nablus, the Marshal of the Hospitallers, entreat the king to give the order to his trumpeters for the charge. Richard was adamant.

'Be patient,' he advised him, 'I tell you, this defensive action must be endured until the time is ripe for an advance when the main Saracen force is exhausted and my delayed reinforcements are here. Then will be the time for action.'

The Marshal returned to the rearguard, where he found the infantry in revolt. The English were praying: 'Saint George! Our patron Saint, will you suffer us to be confounded?'

Some of the French on their knees were entreating the Holy Mother to intercede for them and joined their plea to Saint Denys asking him: 'O Blessed Saint, must we of Christendom perish against this pack of Unbelievers to whom we may not offer battle … Holy Virgin, save us!'

Back again went the Marshal to the king who, having wielded his great battle axe to good purpose, had received a gash on his cheek from the murderous lance of a Turk whose arm he had sliced. He had dismounted from Fauvel, also slightly wounded, and the king had told one of the farrier grooms attendant on the horses, mules and camels to lead Fauvel to safety and fetch him another horse.

The Marshal found the king, momentarily at ease, staunching blood from his face with his unmailed fist. 'Sire, you are wounded!'

'Nothing — a mere scratch. What do you want of me? I have told you I will not attack yet.'

'Sire, my men are in mutiny,' protested Garnier de Nablus. 'I beg you, for God's pity, to give the order for a charge, or they will advance upon the enemy without your word. Forgive them — and me!' With which he wheeled his horse about shouting, 'For Saint George!' and was followed by rank after rank of French and English as he and his brother knights swept down upon the enemy.

Then did Richard, with a shrug and a grin, order the trumpeters to sound the charge, but already the foot soldiers had surged in a torrent behind the vanguard. At once did

Richard mount the horse that had been brought him to replace Fauvel. 'How fares my good Fauvel?' he asked.

'Excellent well, Sire. The farrier has bandaged the wound which is slight, and he says you can ride him tomorrow.'

Reassured, Richard spurred his horse and galloped into the foremost line of Turks with the English and Norman pack behind him triumphantly baying like hounds in the chase.

The Turkish cavalry, taken by surprise by the Crusaders, whom they had thought to be on the defensive and all but ready to surrender, were now in their turn on the defensive. As the Templars, supported by the Hospitallers and foot soldiers, bore down upon them, the Muslims were thrown into confusion at this sudden onslaught from the might of the Christian force. No longer frustrated of their fever to attack and avenge their slaughtered dead, they charged the Turkish centre and left wing as the rearguard swooped upon the right of the Muslim infantry and put them to headlong flight.

'I knew we could do it!' gasped the Marshal of Hospitallers, 'given half a chance and without reinforcements!'

'A whole chance, seemingly,' chuckled Richard, standing in his stirrups to watch the Turks in disorderly retreat.

When all was over the Christians could relax in the encampment on the shore under the evening stars. On the blood-stained sand bodies were piled in heaps awaiting burial of their own fallen men and those of the Saracens.

'And if I,' the Marshal bragged a little to his comrades, 'had not taken it unto myself to charge against the king's orders, all of us would have been on the run!'

But his fellow knights would not have that. 'The king has every right if he chose to hold back the Turks until they were exhausted and *then* to make havoc of them.'

'Which we have done,' he insisted, 'and without reinforcements from the galleys ... Look, here at last they come!'

Huge spectre ships, unlighted lest the Saracen fleet lurking along the coast should sight and waylay them, emerged from the darkening night.

From his encampment on the hillside, above the corpse-littered battlefield, Saladin had watched the disastrous defeat of his household troops, which he had so confidently ranged in the van of his army; but he accepted his defeat as a further proof of his faith in Allah, 'who tests those he has tried the hardest that we be worthy of his trust and be led by trial and our love for him and his Prophet Mahomed to victory.'

It was the best he could do to save his face when he learned from Bohardin, after he had gone down to investigate their losses, that 'Each division has been in worse plight than ever before ... The many of our killed and wounded, far outnumbered the losses of the Christians.'

'Praise be to Allah who thus does try our Faith. We bow to his Almighty judgement and — rejoice,' commented Saladin, whose long upper lip, shaded by the narrow two-winged moustache, and the small pointed beard, its blackness enhancing his yellow pallor, showed little of joy.

Richard was not without sympathy for *the noble Saracens*, as Ambroise, tongue in cheek, recorded, *who have lost in one day more than we have lost in one year...* An excusable exaggeration on the part of Ambroise, who had given up all hope of conquest in that bloodiest of battles since the fall of Acre.

Saladin, resignedly accepting defeat that, for all his vast host, the Crusaders had succeeded where he had failed, did not minimise the quality of *so great a warrior as Ricardus Rex, the Lion Heart*, so Bohardin had it, giving praise where praise was due.

'Not even among our most valiant emirs has been seen such courage and great generalship as that of the English king,' pronounced Saladin; but Bohardin, carefully writing to his Sultan's dictation, disguised in a private postscript the effect the Muslim defeat had upon his master:

Only Allah can know, what intensive grief has filled his heart...

SIX

The Battle of Arsüf was indeed a bitter blow to Saladin, who had counted on a victory that would bring his offensive to a triumphant end; yet it won for Richard ungrudging praise from the Sultan for his skilful handling of greatly inferior forces against the Muslims that outnumbered, as estimated, ten to every one of the Christians.

Richard was the first to recognise that Saladin had proved himself a worthy contender. Mutual admiration may have mitigated, to some extent, the Sultan's disappointment for, apart from transient skirmishes intended to delay the Crusaders' march toward Jerusalem, if the rains fell before Christmas it would hold them back still more. Saladin knew that the Christians must keep their Holy Day, which signified the birth of their god. He discussed with Bohardin his views on the legendary birth of a Jewish girl said to be a virgin, yet she conceived a man child, one Jesus of Nazareth — 'supposed to have been the son of the god they call their father in heaven.'

A thin derisive smile twitched the corners of the Sultan's mouth under the two drooping wings of his moustache. 'But how,' he asked, 'can this fantastic belief that converted almost half the world, and even the civilised Romans ,a thousand years ago — how,' he persisted, 'could they be so convinced of this miraculous conception as to fight now for the belief that a human being could be conceived without intercourse between man and woman? But of course they call this Jesus a god, *born* of a god. It is too naive, is it not? I must admit,' his smile slid sideways, 'that although I have a dozen wives, at least one of them conceived without my assistance, and declared she had never known a man. That too might have been a miracle for, as you know, my harem is well guarded against men. None save my eunuchs may enter there.'

'Yet a eunuch purporting to have been castrated, as befitting your Almighty's purpose to guard your women from all men save yourself, may not Your Highness,' ventured Bohardin, 'have been deceived?'

'How so? Since eunuchs are all medically examined by my personal physicians and pronounced gelded?'

Which proves nothing, thought Bohardin, *if a hand is open for reward to testify illegal intrusion.* But this he did not say aloud. What he did say was, 'This man Jesus, whom the Christians name the Messiah, was prophesied by the Jews as yet to come, although not at the time of the birth which they celebrate on a day in December.'

'The date of the birth of the man who is supposed to be the founder of Christianity, and was himself a Jew, has not been proven,' said Saladin. 'The apostles of this Jesus were a few ignorant fishermen whom he bade follow him and in this very country over which we are now at war, and is presumed to be his birthplace or in its neighbourhood! These fishermen, of whom all have been made saints by their different Popes throughout the ages — their Popes being the heads of their church — these untutored fishermen who could neither read nor write —' an indulgent smile crossed the Sultan's face — 'declared that this Jesus was crucified by the Romans at request of the Jews for claiming to be the son of a god, his father in heaven, and not, I think, until at least fifty years later was his life and death written to be read. He was supposed to have risen from the dead, as you have doubtless heard from those who so firmly believe in him today, yet nothing could have been learned of him except by word of mouth until a Greek doctor — one Luke his name, as I understand — wrote down what he had heard of this Jesus, the son of a carpenter, incarnate in the human shape of a working man. How credulous can so mighty a civilisation as the Romans be! And also the English and French; in fact, almost all Europeans whose culture may be almost on a level with our own.'

'Thus is legend floated into truth,' Bohardin said drily.

'That is so. Even the truth of our Mahomed, whose name is so often ill-spelled by these Christians ... and ourselves, the sons of Allah, we too may be legendary to future centuries. This carpenter's son learned the trade of his father, or foster father, one Joseph of Nazareth, in his workshop, and there is no denying him possessed of an intelligence far above that of the average peasant or working man. Indeed his teaching did eventually convert the whole of the mighty Roman Empire! A great achievement for a Jew,' conceded Saladin, 'and worthy of Mahomed himself. But what we do know of this man Jesus Christ, as they called him and in whose name the Crusaders are at war in the hope to regain Jerusalem, is due to one man and he, strange to say, was a Jew and a confessed anti-Christ! The legend goes that the man Jesus, their acknowledged god, did strike him blind, then opened his eyes to see the Light. He wrote innumerable letters which admittedly are plausible. I have read some of them in the original Greek. His name...'

He paused to recollect, and Bohardin prompted him. 'Was it Saul, All Highest?'

'Ah yes, Saul — changed, I think — to Paul, of Tarsus. They were remarkably intelligent letters, I grant you, but they do not convince me, a son of Allah, our supreme god with whom his prophet Mahomed founded the true faith. Not that Mahomed denied the intelligence of the Christian prophet, their Christ, nor do I, but as for a fifteen-year-old Jewish maiden to whom the Christians pray as the mother of their god in an immaculate conception, that is not the first time such a singular phenomenon has founded a religion.' Saladin paused to help himself to a date offered in a dish of gold by a kneeling slave and continued, 'The Egyptians, a highly civilised culture two or three thousand years before the coming of Jesus, this Christ as they call him and who, I am bound to say, has caused a mort of trouble not only here in our land but in many quarters of the world that has so far been explored!' meditated Saladin, slowly masticating dates — he enjoyed propounding his theories to Bohardin, his sympathetic listener. 'The Egyptians were the first to present a miraculous birth in the form of their god, Osiris, when in the womb with his twin sister Isis, both born, as was said, of the Sun and the Earth. The Greeks also had their gods and goddesses born to Olympian deities, some in the shape of animals ... One could go on for ever...' Saladin's voice dwindled, his head nodded as sleep induced by his lengthy monologues and the consumption of dates, descended ... 'discovering new gods in ... the place of the ... old, but Allah-ah-ah is good enough ... for ... me.'

His head sank. A slave at the entrance to the tent advanced at a gesture from Bohardin, and lifting the now somnolent Sultan's legs, he laid him stretched on his couch with cushions behind his head.

'Bring me my hookah,' commanded Bohardin. 'I too have a fancy to — dream.'

The hookah was brought and Bohardin, whose bed had been made ready for him in the Sultan's tent, inhaled from the bubbling water the hashish-laden smoke, to be wafted into a world of exquisite fantasies.

The Sultan Yusuf Salah-ed-Din was fifty-four at the time of the Third Crusade, and twenty years senior to Richard. His culture, and the nobility of character appreciated by Richard as much as was his statesmanship, were conspicuous in the age of Muslim emergence from semi-barbarism to an intelligence that equalled or surpassed that of Western Europe.

Yet, possibly at the urgent request of Bohardin — always the one adviser who dared to influence him on matters of war or peace — the Sultan, perceiving that Richard was determined to lay siege to Ascalon on his way to Jaffa for Jerusalem, knew that he must either adopt a scorched earth policy in the path of the invaders, or else defeat them in pitched battle.

His emirs, who would not contemplate the capture of a city after the fall of Arsüf, attempted to dissuade the Sultan from further disastrous hostilities. He therefore had to face the destruction of Ascalon, named by Saladin 'the Bride of Syria', rather than lose to the Crusaders more decimation of his armies.

Bohardin, watching his Sultan pacing his tent in an agony of indecision, reported he had said, choking back his tears, 'I would rather sacrifice my children than dislodge one stone of Ascalon. But as Allah wills it — so be it!'

Meanwhile Richard, pursuing his advance toward the Holy City, entered Jaffa, where he encamped to the intense satisfaction of his exhausted army. There he heard of the destruction and evacuation of Ascalon under Saladin's order to the Governor. The unfortunate citizens who suffered the demolition of their homes, and lacking vehicles and horses destroyed in the smoking ruins of the once beautiful city, were forced to go on foot. Some of the few who could not make it either to Egypt or Syria without transport walked, carrying as much as they could manage; mothers with infants in their arms, wailing children at their heels, mules or asses laden with such articles or baskets of food as had been salvaged from their wrecked homes, came at last to Jaffa seeking help.

The refugees were given shelter and food by Richard, who was horrified to learn from them that 'the Bride of Syria' was a pile of ruins. At once he sent his scouts to ascertain the extent of the damage that must have resembled much with which European cities, eight hundred years later, were only too familiar.

But the king's men and his knights were not to be deterred from their relaxation amid the orange groves and orchards in that sun-bewitched land of the Middle East, where, although nearing winter, each blue and golden day was still springlike with blossom.

Visitors from Acre, the wealthy nobles, householders and landowners who had recovered from the surrender of their city to the Crusaders during the previous July, now took their holidays in Jaffa. Unlike Acre's respectable and reputable ladies, there were the same accommodating hostesses here who had entertained the English and Norman Christians in their alcoves at Acre.

And now the houses and streets of Jaffa that had not suffered from the ravages of both the Crusade and Muslim armies resounded to the laughter and singing of the dancing girls and their erotic favours, new to many of the unenlightened English troops but acceptable to the more knowledgeable Franks. Richard — infuriated at the lascivious enjoyment of even his most trusted followers who, as he believed, were immune from the lure of whoredom — gave stern orders that trenches be dug around the walls and the fortification renewed.

'The work of war,' he thundered, 'is your first and only duty to me and to the Cross you carry in the name of our Saviour. All or any of you who so defame our Holy calling shall be dismissed from our service...'

Ambroise, ever ready to report any deviation from the straight and narrow path of virtue to the broader and easier highway of pleasure, averted his eyes from the temptation of unveiled houris, and wrote:

Back to the host the women came
And plied their trade of lust and shame.

But while the majority of knights were chastened by the king's reproaches and his threat to have done with them, there were a number who still hankered after the 'lustful and shameful' excitements of Acre. Richard, however, intended to save Ascalon from utter destruction, hoping to secure the vital road linking Egypt to Syria.

It was the Duke of Burgundy who, in command of the French since the desertion of Philip, his king, attempted to persuade Richard that the shortest route to Jerusalem would be their present halt at Jaffa. This, he argued, would dispense with the problem of pursuing the more difficult way inland, passing villages and castles that Saladin had destroyed to obstruct the Crusaders' advance.

Torn between Burgundy's urgent advice and that of his Crusaders — who, apart from re-fortifying the town could, despite the king's commands, continue to enjoy the pleasures of Jaffa — Richard began to wonder, in view of the arguments put to him by Burgundy and those of his latest favourite, one of the French knights, William des Préaux, if it were better to suggest temporary peace terms to Saladin while he waited for further reinforcements. In this state of indecision he wrote to Bernard, Abbot of Clairvaux, who was with Richard's wife and sister at Acre:

Having spent not only all our money but our strength and flesh too, we signify to you our utter inability to stay in Syria beyond Easter ... Wherefore, falling on our knees, we pray with tears and prayers to stir up the chiefs and noblemen and folk throughout all Christendom to the service of the Living God ... For with His favour we shall hold the defence of God's heritage and we shall win...

In this letter to the Abbot Richard hinted at his doubts as to whether he could organise a successful advance until after Easter — if then, or ever! There were still some two months to go before Christmas while he waited for more reinforcements from the galleys ... and now he learned that Conrad of Montferrat at Tyre had taken upon himself to make overtures of peace with Saladin!

'Unknown to me!' he stormed to Burgundy, striding up and down his tent. 'The bare-faced presumption of it! Without an order from *me*!' This news of Conrad's audacity had aroused in Richard his hot Plantagenet temper. 'That he should dare — I'll —' His words choked him. His face, suffused with red, gave Burgundy to fear he was on the verge of apoplexy, but it was impossible to attempt appeasement with him in this state.

Inquisitive knights, hearing the raging voice of the king, came from their tents to ask, 'What now has bitten him?'

'I'll not stir from here,' they heard. (That, at any rate, would keep them to their various enjoyments for the present.) 'I'll have Conrad's head on a pike before I will allow him to take —' another splutter of rage choked him — 'to take the law into his own hands — to treat with Saladin against me! I'll stay here, by God I will, until I can slay this devilish Conrad who hates me even more than I hate him. We are still outnumbered by Saladin's infidels, and until my reinforcements arrive I'll not budge an inch. I,' he thumped his chest, 'I and I *alone* will confront Saladin with my terms of peace — and I'll deal with Montferrat — to see him hanged!'

'So much for Conrad,' chuckled the knights who had no liking for the Marquis of Montferrat. Some had come to words, if not to blows, with him for his high-handedness. 'As if in command of Tyre,' they said, 'as he has taken command of the king!'

Yes, so much for Conrad, but not enough for Richard. This defiance of his authority had given rise to a stratagem lain dormant, until he decided to pursue his purpose with Saladin that had already been inducted, although against his wishes, by Conrad.

'But what I first must do,' he told Burgundy, 'is to return to Acre and bring my wife and sister here that we may celebrate Christmas together.'

'Ah, yes, indeed,' assented Burgundy, relieved, for there was no knowing what His Grace would do as a result of this unfortunate affair of Montferrat. Did he intend to forsake the Crusades as Philip, his king, had done? Or would he hand in a truce to the Sultan to gain time before the final advance?

Cautiously he probed, 'Will Your Grace be taking a company of your knights with you, Sire?'

'Only those whom I always choose to accompany me on a non-combatant journey.'

I am evidently de trop, said the duke to his inner man. *God knows what he will encounter on the way if he intends to go by road…*

He did intend to go by road, and Burgundy was uneasily reminded of the severe action with which the Frankish armies had contended when, day after broiling day, they had toiled on to Haifa over Mount Carmel and on to Caesarea, always meeting with Saladin's forces and doggedly combating their superior numbers until the fiercest fight of all at Arsüf.

But how could he be so foolhardy as to risk it again? thought Burgundy. Saladin had burnt the ground to ashes, crops and villages destroyed. Where to find the food for his escort, and how to combat Muslims in ambush on the way, with only a handful of knights?

'I see,' grinned Richard divining Burgundy's misgivings, 'that you think I am courting a hornet's nest.'

Pray God it be a mare's nest, inly said the duke; and to the king: 'Your Grace has never failed in your undertakings.'

'What I undertake now,' said Richard, 'is to bring my wife to me.'

After his tempestuous outburst, he wondered how, without committing himself to a pacific termination of hostilities with Saladin, he could gain time to pursue his plan — but of course, he decided, Joan would have to be brought into it. He foresaw — he chuckled — a blaze of fireworks from her when he broached a subject he had in mind. He brooded on it while he sought relaxation from immediate problems in his favourite sport of falconry.

He had brought with him his falcons in the mews of one of his galleys that had not suffered disasters of storm. So with a company of knights he went hawking, and took the opportunity to reconnoitre to see how the land lay between Jaffa and the road to Jerusalem.

And here he met with an adventure that might have cost him the end of his Crusade, if not his life.

His falcons had served him well to recover bountiful quarry when, exhausted with his day's sport, he told his knights he would rest and bade them do the same. Choosing the shade of a cypress he fell asleep and was awakened by the thunder of hooves and the familiar war cry of 'Allah — Allahooh!'

At once he roused his sleeping companions. They slept more soundly than their king, who always maintained he slept like a dog with one eye open. 'Up!' he shouted. 'Get up! The Saracens are at us!'

They had been on the watch for any such chance to make a surprise attack, and at once rushed full gallop at the king and would have taken him prisoner had not William des Préaux yelled at them, 'Hold! He is not Malek Ric! *I* am the king!'

The ruse worked. Had they seized Richard they would have risked severe punishment from their Sultan, whose strict orders were never to attack or imprison the person of his royal adversary any more than the king's men would seize or attack himself, the All Highest.

Dismayed, the two who had seized Richard released him; and despite he was unarmoured, as were his knights in their hawking suits, and carried no weapons save swords or daggers, they charged at the Muslims. Richard mounted Fauvel, who was quietly grazing nearby, and snatched up his battle axe, without which he would never venture beyond his camp. Brandishing his dreaded weapon, which the more superstitious Muslims believed held magic qualities that could slay at sight, he and his followers made short work of the dozen or so Saracens. They, having seen the party at rest, had hoped for an easy conquest.

All was soon over — but, to Richard's horror, not without the killing of two knights. The Scot, the A'Hannach, one of the company and an ardent falconer, saved des Préaux from capture while he cried to the king, 'Sire, save yourself! Without you, Christendom is lost!'

Whether he heard him or not, Richard, uttering his terrifying war cries, routed the few remaining Saracens who had not yet been scattered, and returned to des Préaux to find him in the arms of the young Scot, and bleeding severely.

'Help me get him on my horse,' he bade the Scot. Between them they lifted him. The A'Hannach tore a strip of linen from his surtout and staunched the wound as best he could. The two dead knights were also borne away on their horses, and the sad procession went back to their camp at Jaffa.

'A sorry day for us,' lamented Richard, 'to have lost my two brave knights...' He had also lost a jewelled belt retrieved by des Préaux before he fell. Richard had him brought to his own tent and himself bathed the wound, then sent for Garnier de Noblas, Master of the Hospitallers and a skilled surgeon.

After examining the injury the Master pronounced it superficial. The loss of blood, he said, had dispensed with the necessity of leeches and had cleansed the wound. Within a few days des Préaux had recovered and to him Richard presented a belt, a wedding gift from his wife.

'As you already bear the arms of knighthood,' he told him, 'I cannot knight you again for your courage, but I can give you this in token of my gratitude for saving my life.' He wound the jewelled belt round the knight's middle and bade him, 'Wear it in token of my love...'

It was a sultry day in October, the skies heavy with promise of rain; and Berengaria, as Joan resignedly suffered, had been more than ever tiresome and full of complaints.

'This abominable food is fit only for the pig trough, and what with the flies and the fleas —'

'No fleas, child,' Joan said sharply. 'Your women are far too careful, and forever chiding the slaves to keep all free from dirt and vermin. We are lucky to be housed here at Acre in comparative comfort. Think what Richard has had to put up with living, as his courier reports to me, in a tent; and as for dirt and,' she shuddered, 'scorpions and refuse thrown out, with no means of ridding it save for the vultures — and set upon by Saracens when out hawking, as I have been told happened to him a week or two ago — wonder it is he's still alive.'

'And more wonder,' grumbled Berengaria, 'that *we* are still alive.' She flung back her long unbraided hair that had escaped its fillet. 'O, God! How I *wish* I had never been dragged here, married against my will, shipwrecked — or almost — in those dreadful storms. Why, oh *why* was I made to follow the Crusade? I am not a Crusader. What is it to me whether Richard takes Jerusalem or not? I want —' she covered her face, and her small body shook with sobs — 'I want to go home to Navarre. I ought never to have been brought here. I didn't want to be married — not to Richard — not to *him*. He's too old for me and — ugly. My women think he's handsome. I've seen handsomer bullocks. And as for treating me as his wife, I might just as well be married to a eunuch. I'm sick — sick — *sick* of him and you, and of everyone here in this Godforsaken heathen land, and not a soul to talk to of my own age. All my women are as old and ugly as Richard — chosen by the Queen Mother, I suppose, lest Richard should want to bed with any of them were she under sixty! Not that he would ever want to bed with a woman, least of all with me ... I want to go *home*!' So on and repetitively on, until Joan was hard put to hold her hand from assault on her sister queen's ear.

It was for the fifth or sixth time that Berengaria had continued her complaint concerning her objection to being imprisoned here 'among a lot of savages, and I blame my father for marrying me to a man who spends his life cutting up Saracens with his awful battle axe, and I hope I'll be killed by one of them rather than live in such *hell*!'

This Richard overheard in a torrent of Basque French when, having arrived at the palace, he strode on in advance of his knights and thrusting aside a servant who would have announced him, entered the apartment of his sister and his queen.

'So! If this is your hell I can promise you heaven when I take you back to England — with me!'

He advanced to his startled wife and, catching her up in his arms, swung her off her feet and round about, while Joan ran to him crying, 'Thank God! We feared you — out hawking — but now you are safe — we dared not think — oh, Heavenly Grace!' Between this coherent welcome, and shrieks from the whirling Berengaria: 'Put me down — you make me giddy. Beast — you *beast*! Let me go!' while regrettably, her feet in the air, she kicked his shins.

'I'll never let you go,' he laughed as he lowered her still in his arms. 'I've come to take and keep you here,' he pulled her to his heart, 'where you belong.'

'I don't — I won't —' She struggled to free herself as he stooped his mouth to hers, and dodged his kiss. 'No, don't — I don't like you — you smell!'

'Smell?' he roared. 'Of what do I smell?'

'Of horse and — and dung — and blood from your killing. I wouldn't mind joining in a fight against the infidels but I hate war — and I hate you! And I want,' the litany began again, 'I want to go *home*!'

'So you shall go home,' with exemplary patience, Richard soothed her, 'home with me to my home, a castle in England. I have only seen it once. It is at a place called Windsor and it stands on the banks of a great river — the Thames, and I will see it for the second time with you, my love.'

'I am not your love,' muttered Berengaria. 'You have only one love and that is war — if it isn't your troubadour Ambroise, or that other one, Blondel, whom you left with us here to play on his lute and sing to us. Much you care about *me*, your wife. Why, oh why did you ever marry me?'

This prevailing whine went unheard or ignored by Richard, for Joan was at him to say in a cautionary whisper, 'I have had bad news from England. I didn't want to harass you with more anxieties about your neglected kingdom, until —' Then, abruptly rounding on the sulky-mouthed Berengaria: 'Go, my dear, and tell the servants to prepare dinner for Richard and the knights, and the state rooms for the king.'

As Berengaria went, with dragging steps and a baleful glance at her husband, Joan said, 'I hope to heaven you will take her back to England so soon as may be. She is a perpetual nuisance. You should never have brought her here.'

Richard lowered himself into a chair and stooped to unfasten the leathern thongs of his *chausses,* the cross-gartered hose of cloth fitted with footwear as worn by the Norman knights. On his journey from Jaffa he had gone unarmoured save for a suit of mail under his surtout, as always when not habited for battle, that he might not be recognised should he encounter the enemy. Then, barefoot and with a sigh of contentment, he leaned back in the chair. 'That's better. My good Fauvel went lame for the last three miles, so I walked him.'

'Could you not have taken one of your knights' horses?' objected Joan. 'You are always more considerate of their comfort than of your own.'

'I am never too considerate of those who lay down their lives for me, and these few of my comrades I have brought here are all battle-scarred, and some of them are lame as my horse … Well, what is this bad news from England?'

'Our mother sends me word, not knowing where you are or might be, that John is stirring up *more* trouble, this time against Longchamp to whom you gave, I think unwisely, too much authority. John is strongly opposed to Longchamp, who seeks supreme power — Why do you look so bored?'

'Because you tell me nothing I don't already know, and only what our mother reported to me when I met her at Messina with Berengaria. I sent Bishop Walter, my faithful Hubert, to deal with any difficulties — *and* with John — in my absence.'

'Yes, I know all about that, but it is now becoming urgent. You are so set upon this Crusade that you neglect your duty to your kingdom. There is no knowing what John will do. He is always plotting in his sly underhand way to work against you with Philip of France. Ever since you refused to marry Alais, Philip has been determined to avenge himself on you for having — as he tells everyone — jilted her in favour of Berengaria. And now John suggests *he* should marry Alais!'

Richard gave a shrug. 'Bigamy doesn't deter our John from taking to himself a future queen consort while he has one lawful wife. All this tittle-tattle is no news to me. I will return to England and settle my affairs there when I have settled my affair *here*, which is to lay myself at the feet of the Holy

Sepulchre before I take John by his ear and stand him in the corner for stealing conserve from our nursery cupboard as I used to do!'

'How *can* you take it so lightly?' Joan protested impatiently. 'Do you not see the danger you and the kingdom are in?'

'Have no fear on my account,' Richard told her. 'John has no more power to injure me, or my kingdom, than he had in our nursery days when he would lie on his back and kick and scream if he couldn't get his own way.'

'You have always spoilt him, as you spoil that girl of yours.'

'That girl of mine,' Richard broke into a chuckle, 'will come with me when I go back to England, my home that has never *been* my home. And if I have any more of her tantrums I'll lay her across my knee, as I did to John when he was naughty, and give her what —' he yawned widely — 'she ... deserves, and if she has had my room prepared for me I'll not wait for a meal. I'll ... a-ah ... to bed.'

A week after Richard's unexpected arrival at Acre he took his two queens back with him to Jaffa. There he found the galleys and the further reinforcements for which he had been waiting. He then proceeded to start negotiations for the plan he had conceived whereby he could propose terms with Saladin for peace. That these would not be acceptable he fully realised: none the less, he could gain time for his victorious advance upon Jerusalem.

Accordingly, as a preliminary token of goodwill, he presented Malek el Adil (Saphadin) the Sultan's brother, with a magnificent horse, one of those that had come in his shipments. A few days later from Yazur, where Saphadin was encamped, came a message of effusive thanks. Richard then sent the envoy back with two peace proposals, one to be sent to Saladin, the other for Saphadin in confidence.

To Saladin he wrote: *Greetings to the All Highest, O, my letter!* And followed this up with a lament concerning the circumstances of both the Muslim and Franks, reduced now in men and goods to their last resources. *Surely,* he wrote, *we have had enough of this unhappy state of affairs. It is only left to us to gain Jerusalem and the Holy Cross. However,* (an artful dodge this) *we are resolved not to renounce Jerusalem so long as we have one single man left to us … But as regards the Holy Cross, to you it is nothing more than a worthless bit of wood whereas to us it is our life … You, Sultan, will be doing us a great favour to restore it …* He ended, optimistically, *in the hope that all will come right of itself and that we shall enjoy a pleasant rest after our long toil.*

To this Saladin replied that Jerusalem was as precious to him as it was to Malek Ric, since it had been from there that the Prophet made his journey to heaven (this the first Richard had heard of that heavenly voyage), and the Sultan went on to insist that the land belonged originally to Islam and not to the kings of England.

Hardly encouraging was this: *And moreover when in the past you seized your Holy City,* Richard was reminded (no soft words here to sweeten the pill), *it was only because of the weakness of the Muslim forces who at that time, were unable to hold it against superior strength.*

Regarding the Cross, Saladin made it clearly understood that its possession was no *'worthless piece of wood'* to Islam, but a very profitable advantage.

'God's Throat!' fumed Richard. 'Does he mean to sell it to Levantine Jews?'

But he still held what he thought to be a trump card to play against Saphadin, by which Saladin, who opposed all suggestions to render up Jerusalem, might yet be won by an astonishing concession.

This Richard proposed in his confidential letter to Saphadin that he, the Sultan's brother, should marry the widowed sister of the English king! In which case they would live and reign together in Jerusalem. What more agreeable offer could be made, with the added inducement of Acre, Jaffa, and Ascalon and the freedom of all Muslim and Christian prisoners in exchange for the Holy Cross that meant all the world to Christians and less than nothing to Islam?

Saphadin received this surprising offer with ecstatic gratitude. To be the husband of the widowed Queen of Sicily and the brother — or as good as brother — of the king Malek Ric, was beyond his wildest dreams, a blessing surely from Mahomed and not to be refused by him, the merest cypher in the Kingdom of the All Highest!

At once he sent for Bohardin and entrusted him with the letter from Malek Ric to be conveyed to Salah-ed-Din.

When Saladin read it he roared with laughter, as reported by Bohardin, and although he saw through Richard's confidence trick by which he hoped to gain his ends in using Saphadin as his decoy, he graciously agreed to consider it. While still laughing up his voluminous sleeve at the outrageous proposition, he sent Bohardin back to Malek Ric with an acknowledgement of the honour proposed by the great English king to his brother, but he refrained from any commitment.

It was Richard's turn to laugh, believing he had succeeded in bluffing the All Highest as Saladin had bluffed him, the 'All Lowest'. But he ceased to laugh when Joan, informed how she had been offered as wife to the Sultan's brother, fell into a towering rage, as Richard ruefully recounted to Ambroise, and attacked the king — whether physically as well as verbally is not known — yet in view of the Plantagenet temper we may reconstruct the scene something like this:

Joan burst in upon Richard in the apartment of the castle he had taken at Jaffa when his ship came with equipments and building materials for the restoration of the town destroyed by Saladin during his burnt earth policy.

Richard, seated at a table, was poring over a map he had drawn indicating the shortest route to Jerusalem. 'So near and yet so far,' he muttered, tracing with a finger the mileage from Jaffa through Ramleh and Emmaus and so on to the Holy City. 'No easy way,' he continued, regardless of Joan hovering in a very tempest of fury above him, 'and Saladin's defences bristling with the forts he has erected to hold us back … I let him think we have nothing left for reprisals and that our men are reduced to starvation with no crops from the burnt earth. Let him think so! I'll wager he'll be glad enough to come to peace with Joan as burnt offering!'

'What in hell,' screamed Joan, 'are you mumbling about? Me — a burnt offering? For God's sake, are you run mad? Do you think I'm a widowed Hindu woman to be burnt alive?'

'Mad? Hindu?' Richard, still immersed in the study of his map, asked absently; and then, as if just aware of her presence, 'What do you want?'

'You!' She pointed a trembling finger and let forth a torrent of hysterical abuse. 'You — to dare offer me — *me* — to wive with an infidel! How can you sink yourself, and me, so low? What do you think to gain by such —' she spluttered — 'such infamous, sacrilegious — you, a Christian! I would sooner die — and *you* — I'd sooner *kill* you than see you disgrace yourself by so degrading and infamous —' The words spouting from her like a storm of hailstones were suddenly checked as, raising a fist, she would have brought it down upon Richard's head had he not caught her wrist in attempted placation.

'Why all this? Do you really suppose I would have you wed with Saphadin? I only made the suggestion guessing he would fall into it headlong and discuss it with Saladin and decide what to do. I knew Saladin would never agree, but could gain time while they —'

'Stop!' Wrenching herself free, she made as if to come at him again. 'Don't give me these futile excuses! I know what you planned — never mind me — so long as you could make Saladin believe you were ready for truce by handing me over — *me,* the Queen of Sicily — to a heathen Unbeliever! You and your Crusade — the devil's Crusade for sure, and you his apostle, God save us!'

Again her fist descended, but he dodged that one and, rising, caught her by the shoulders and shook her till her teeth rattled.

'You whoreson fool!' he shouted. 'Do you believe I ever intended you to wed with one of them? You don't begin to understand the intricacies of political warfare and the scheming by which we can throw dust in the enemy's eyes and trample him down as Saladin contrives against me. He has more sense in one of his fingernails than any one of my advisers, and if he were a Christian I'd gladly give you up to him, though I doubt he'd have you since he looks for more than a woman has to offer as a wife, were he blessed by the Grace of our God. As it is, I will suggest to Saphadin that he can take half of all I have won from Saladin in exchange for you, if he will turn Christian.'

'Then,' she had paled, looking at him long and searchingly, 'you *are* mad. I will ask the Master of the Hospitallers to have you watched and guarded. Is this the end of your Crusade, and you in a straitjacket instead of a coat of mail?'

'More likely,' he uttered a loud guffaw, 'that a Muslim prince would make you wear a chastity belt over your private parts if he were changed into a Christian. But you had best take yourself and my wife back to Acre to be out of the way, for Saphadin is going to hold a banquet at his encampment in honour of his betrothal, as I am informed. He will, of course, expect *you*, his promised bride, as well as myself, to be present.'

'God damn you!' yelled Joan. 'Go then to his banquet and may he give you poison in your drink!'

Needless to say, Joan, with Berengaria and the child princess of Cyprus, made all haste to Acre. From there Joan endeavoured to procure transport to take her and her two charges to France or England, 'or anywhere,' she told Berengaria, to whom she had confided Richard's intended disposal of her to 'that yellow-faced heathen. Can you conceive of such a monstrous act of cruelty and sacrilege against me — his sister?'

'More than sacrilege — a sacrifice!' Berengaria would believe anything defamatory of Richard. 'I don't doubt he would offer *me* to Saphadin if he could persuade Saladin to render up Jerusalem. Not only is he mad — he is bad. Yes, we will go back to my country or yours — or to Rome where I can plead with his Holiness, the Pope, that my marriage to a madman be dissolved.'

Joan felt inclined to support her sister-in-law in this drastic decision, since she realised how Richard's wife, who was no wife, felt herself to be slighted, unloved and unwanted.

Meanwhile Richard, having sent his troublesome womenfolk back to Acre, proceeded to follow up his tactics by which he could throw dust in his enemy's eyes with his preposterous plan to arrange a marriage with Joan and the 'yellow-faced heathen'. How such a proposition could have aided his capture of Jerusalem he may not have yet decided; however, he kept up a pretence of the absurd negotiations, and duly attended the banquet prepared for the King of England and Saphadin's prospective bride. She, unfortunately, as conveyed to the Muslim prince with many apologies from Richard, was unable to attend owing to a regrettable attack of fever. In return, and with similar regrets, she was sent by her betrothed a magnificent diamond ring which she immediately flung down the privy.

The betrothal banquet ordered by Saphadin lacked nothing of splendour, although it was held in a tent or rather three tents joined to make one in a kind of large marquee. As Saphadin was in charge of a regiment his encampment had to serve as a place of entertainment.

The edibles supplied, of great delicacy to Muslim taste, might not have appealed to that of his guest Malek Ric, whose Frankish chef could never have contrived such gastronomic delights as toads' tongues, if not unfamiliar with the legs of frogs. There were platters of silver that contained bundles of pallid concoctions swathed in vine leaves; these his host pressed upon Richard saying he must eat of at least one of them, which were the testicles of a bull soaked in wine and flavoured with a she-goat's urine, second only as an aphrodisiac to the lampreys with which the banquet would end.

Richard gratefully accepted and managed to dispose of these in the silken napkin that accompanied each dish on which to wipe his greasy fingers, since knives and forks were at that time unknown in both Christian and Muslim countries. But the main course of the feast was roast camel described by the ubiquitous Ambroise, who accompanied his king as equerry, and reported it *a savoury flesh when larded well and flesh roasted.*

After plentiful wine — if forbidden by the followers of the Prophet — was enjoyed to the full by Richard, girls were brought to the tent and a floor cleared to display themselves in erotic dance and more song, of which Malek Ric fortunately understood no word.

And now, since it was obvious that Saladin would never agree to Richard's iniquitous suggestion for an alliance between his sister and Saphadin, there were no Christmas festivities. Joan and Berengaria had returned to Acre, and Richard was faced with more delay to his final advance upon Jerusalem by the appalling weather. Unceasing rains had made an impassable swamp of the road to Ramleh, the first halt on the way to the Holy City.

At a council of war held on 12 January, the Templars and Hospitallers pointed out the inadvisability of laying siege to Jerusalem under these present conditions. Against Richard's fiery objections that he would see them and himself in hell if he would hold back the forces he had gathered for this last and triumphant siege, the Duke of Burgundy, seconding the Templars' proposal, said that as Saladin still held the city against a siege, he was in a stronger position with regard to supplies than the Christians. If the majority did reach their goal they would starve before the Saracens gave up; they were well fortified with recent caravans from Cairo.

Having worn himself out with furious vituperation against Burgundy, the Marshal of the Hospitallers and the 'whole damn lot of them', Richard at last agreed to a temporary retirement that would cover the next twenty miles back to Ascalon. This came as a fearful blow to the army, with their hope of victory in the near future shattered by the interference of the Templars and Hospitallers. So dismayed were they that they refused to return to Ascalon which, it had been decided, would be the likeliest place to wait for better weather conditions to their pilgrimage.

In mutiny against the order that held them from the goal on which they had set their hearts, many threw themselves down in the slush and mud left from the snows of the mountains to melt in torrential rains. They were prepared to die rather than forsake their cause, since they did not believe the king would now continue his Crusade.

But Richard, assuring them his retirement was only a temporary measure and that when more food and equipment for which he had sent urgent messages should arrive, persuaded them to follow him. Those that were too sick and exhausted to march he ordered to be carried in litters, although some of the poor horses, weakened from want of fodder and the hardships of transit, collapsed and died and were left to the vultures.

After the retiring army had reached Ramleh a number of the disgruntled French returned to Jaffa and Acre while others joined Conrad at Tyre. And here was another problem for Richard to face: Conrad, in scarcely disguised enmity with his king — and, as Richard suspected, in league against him with Saladin — was again making trouble.

When Richard and his wearied forces reached Ascalon they found the once beautiful city in ruins. Saladin had kept his word that he would sooner see his lovely 'Bride of Syria' destroyed than surrendered to the Christians. The work of rebuilding the walls, crumbled to dust and piles of brick, was shared by all from the slaves to the servants, from knights and barons to the King of the Lion Heart, who took the lion's share of the heaviest work, lugging great stones and fallen beams to set an example to those who laid down tools from sheer exhaustion due to the long march from Jaffa through swamps and mud.

Rebuilding operations were well under way, and several houses rendered habitable for Richard and his suite, when he decided to communicate with Conrad de Montferrat, insisting that he render military service to the Crusade and so end this senseless feud he had brought against the king.

Conrad therefore agreed to meet Richard at a place between Acre and Tyre, but as result of this appointment, Conrad defiantly refused to serve the Crusade. At once Richard in a fury let him know that he must forfeit the revenues of Jerusalem, which he had hoped would be his were he elected nominal king in place of Guy de Lusignan. Whereupon, according to Hovenden, Conrad gave out with smug complacency that the king had left him *very sad and ill at ease*...

Richard was still more ill at ease when a messenger arrived from England with letters from Longchamp urging him to return *on the wings of the wind* ... an ill wind that blew no good when followed by a letter from the Queen Mother saying that Philip intended to invade Normandy and recover his sister from the tower at Rouen, where she had been kept a virtual prisoner. Eleanor did not explain why, or by whom, Alais had been kept in custody, but Richard guessed it must have been John, who had declared his intention of making the Princess of France his wife and imprisoned her so that no other prince could have the chance to offer himself as suitor.

This latest news Richard imparted to Ambroise, all agog to hear more of it. 'There will be no more of it,' he was informed, 'until I have made my final advance upon Jerusalem.' *And also,* he added (but only to himself), *until I have dealt with Conrad.*

As for John, he would deal with him so soon as he returned to England and saw exactly how the wind blew there. He had not heard from Bishop Walter of any later developments.

But when another letter from the Queen Mother implored him to return to England 'with all speed and to abandon all projects' (*meaning my Crusade,* was his glum conjecture) 'and save himself and his kingdom from John who was waiting to seize the crown', he felt impelled to call a council meeting to discuss his departure.

When he told the assembled knights and barons of his intention, a gasp of dismay as of a sudden breeze swept through the crowded room. 'Which being so,' continued Richard, brusquely, 'I will leave three hundred knights and two thousand men-at-arms to serve in my kingdom of Jerusalem in my absence.'

This raised the question of who should wear the Crown of Jerusalem as Viceroy until such as the king should claim his own. Should it be Conrad of Montferrat or Guy de Lusignan?

Richard, in extreme doubt as to the advisability of Conrad acting as his deputy, agreed to put it to the vote — de Lusignan or Montferrat? And Conrad was elected by a large majority to reign over Jerusalem in the king's name.

When the news of this was brought to Conrad at Tyre, he, in a frenzy of thanksgiving, was on his knees beseeching God to make him worthy of the honour to wear the Crown of Jerusalem, and that if he were found to be unworthy the crown should be denied him.

Meanwhile Richard had announced his immediate intention of returning to England, yet he could not bring himself to give up all hope of his entry into Jerusalem when he had only about forty more miles to go before he reached the gates of the Holy City.

The rains were over and the glorious spring of the Near East danced in the orange and olive groves when Richard and his army, now replenished with the reinforcements for which he had been waiting, marched to Blanchegarde. His Templars and Hospitallers rejoiced to be on their pilgrimage again, led by Richard; it had been a bitter disappointment when they heard that their king would leave them to finish the Crusade without him.

Very different was this march from the miserable conditions they had undergone when leaving Jaffa for Ascalon. In their renewed strength of men and arms they confidently attacked the fortress of Blanchegarde, on the shortest route to Jerusalem.

The Turks stationed in the garrison fled at the approach of the formidable army led by Malek Ric brandishing his terrible axe, which, it was said by those who had the misfortune to meet him in battle, could slay ten men at one blow.

After the victorious rout of the garrison Richard gave his knights another shock. He would return to Ascalon — just for the day and night — alone.

Against all persuasion that he must not venture on the journey unaccompanied, he refused attendance. 'Every one of you,' he told them, 'must remain here. I do not trust Saladin keeping eternal watch on us from every hill and tower, not to attack with his hundreds of Saracens. Not one of you can be spared. Never fear for me. It is barely seventeen miles to Ascalon. I'll be back with you at dawn tomorrow.'

But several dawns had come and gone before Richard returned to Blanchegarde. To begin with, the comparatively short journey to Ascalon on his trusty Fauvel was help up by combat with a wild boar that rushed at him from the woods bordering the road. Richard snatched his battle axe, without which he never travelled, and even as the huge beast reared to drag him from the saddle he was down and bringing the axe in one blow upon the boar's great head. Yet it was not done for, and while Richard dodged the fearful jaws snarled back against its tusks that dripped a gory flow from the gash on its head, the brute was at him again; but Richard managed to finish it off with another smashing blow that scattered its blood and brains in the dust at the reared feet of Fauvel.

'All's well, lad,' Richard comforted his terrified stallion. 'He'll not trouble us now, but pity 'tis we can't have boar's head for supper.' And with soothing pats of the satin-smooth neck Richard went on his way.

Upon his arrival at Ascalon he was met by the Marshal of Hospitallers whom he had left in charge of the restored garrison. He had grave news to give him. Conrad had been killed — murdered as he left the house of the Bishop of Beauvais, who had held a feast in honour of his election as nominal King of Jerusalem.

While Richard sat at supper, he learned how Conrad had been waylaid by two men disguised as mendicants in rags with pitiful pleas for alms and, even as Conrad searched his pouch for money to give them in pity for their plight, he was seized and stabbed to lie where he had fallen with a dagger in his heart.

It took some little time for the 'Assassins', so named for the fanatical religious cult they represented, to be caught and tried for murder. It seemed that this atrocity had been instigated by the chief of the Assassins, one Rashid ed Din, more familiarly known as the 'Old Man of the Mountain'.

The word 'Assassin' derived from the Arabic *hashish,* and it was thought that under the influence of the drug, awful deeds were perpetrated in a supposedly political and religious cause.

As many of their acts of violence were performed by stealth, and prominent Muslims or Christians were always their victims, it was assumed that Conrad was their lawful — or unlawful — prey. All were grist to Rashid's revolutionary mill whomsoever he hoped to grind to his own heretical beliefs that there was no God, no Prophet, no Christian Saviour. He enticed his disciples to follow him with the promise of an afterlife wherein they would enjoy eternal peace and pleasure, and so bade them seek and prefer death to that of heaven with a mythical God or Mahomed. At the lift of a finger, a nod of his head, men would swear fidelity to him and were his 'truly blessed' to kill disbelievers and to kill themselves with the knives their Sheikh offered them as consecrated to the murder of Muslims, Christians, or whomsover bowed to any faith but his … Such were the tales that went the round of Syria to plant horrific fear in the hearts of the simple-minded.

When the two Assassins were caught, one was executed and the other tied to the tail of a horse and dragged through the streets of Tyre until he died, a favoured type of punishment by Muslims and Christians alike. But although the Assassin confessed to have been the murderer of Conrad, hoping by that to have been pardoned, it was generally believed that the King of England had contrived the death of Montferrat.

This suspicion was brought to Richard by the Marshal of Hospitallers, who begged him to return to Blanchegarde, for his life here would be in danger. Richard, the Marshal reminded him, was the obvious one to implicate, since all knew of the enmity between him and Conrad.

In the meantime the garrison at Blanchegarde was in greatest anxiety concerning their king. When, after forty-eight hours, he had not returned as promised, they feared some catastrophe must have befallen him. He had been set upon by Saracens, captured to lie rotting in a dungeon of one of Saladin's castles, eaten by rats or the horrific widow spiders whose bite was certain death ... This the macabre belief of Ambroise; but Roger de Glanville, the knight whom Richard had left in charge of the fort at Blanchegarde, refuted that, for, said he, neither Saladin nor the king would attack and capture the other's royal person. The battle for the Holy City must be fought between the Crusaders and the Muslims, never between the two kings.

However, in fear lest their king had abandoned them and left for England — or, worse still, had been seized by Muslims or robbers and killed — it was decided that de Glanville, accompanied by an armed cavalry, must go in search of their leader.

So in due course, while the Marshal was urging Richard to return to Blanchegarde attended by the Knights of St John, de Glanville arrived at Ascalon. On learning of this latest crisis and their king's danger of involvement, that although an alibi could at once be proved since he had been nowhere near Tyre at the time of the murder, de Glanville suggested that a letter purporting to have been written by Rashid of the Mountain should be sent to Leopold of Austria. He was the most likely to implicate Richard, being at daggers drawn with him owing to that business of Leopold's banner displanted during the siege of Acre. It was therefore proposed that the Duke of Austria, leader of the German Crusade, slighted by England, should be informed of the innocence of Richard and so dispel all dangerous rumours. Not that this ruse could entirely vindicate the English king.

Since it became known that Richard intended to return to England before the campaign was over, the French, who had always deplored his rejection of their Princess Alais, were now more than ever resentful. Bad enough that their own king had deserted the Crusade, but that the leader of them all should think of renouncing his Holy Pilgrimage gave further cause for the French to fear the worst.

Hostility now was rife against Richard among the French Crusaders no less than the men of Tyre and followers of Conrad, their late Governor.

When Henry of Champagne, nephew of Richard, offered himself to and was accepted by Isabelle, the twenty-year-old widow of Conrad, and married to Henry within a week of her husband's murder, the French were convinced the marriage had been arranged by Richard.

Isabelle, twice widowed, was an enviable match. By the death of her elder sister Sibylla, the wife of Guy de Lusignan, Isabelle had inherited the kingdom of Jerusalem. How this inheritance came about, none was very clear, but before her marriage to Guy de Lusignan, Sibylla had been the wife of the deceased King of Jerusalem, Baldwin IV. When he died, Sibylla's son by a former husband — or, more likely, a lover — became Baldwin V of Jerusalem and died a helpless invalid soon after his crowning. This left the throne free — for whom? For Sibylla and her latest husband, Guy de Lusignan.

After the death of Sibylla, her young sister Isabelle became the wife of Conrad Montferrat. And now, with Conrad dead, Henry of Champagne — hastily married to Isabelle, nominal Queen of Jerusalem — could claim to be, with her, joint ruler of the Holy City.

That Henry was also the nephew of King Philip gave the French one more grievance to hold against King Richard, who had obviously manoeuvred Henry's marriage with the Queen of Jerusalem to benefit his nephew, and so prevent his other uncle, King of France, from offering *his* nephew to Isabelle.

Although her queenship could only be nominal until Richard had fulfilled his mission and captured Jerusalem for himself and his heirs — if any — did not mitigate the growing resentment fostered by the French against the English king.

So no wonder that these damaging suspicions, whether groundless or not, hastened Richard back to Blanchegarde. From there, and against all advice from his mother and Longchamp, he renewed his advance upon Jerusalem to capture the Holy City and realise his whole life's dream.

SEVEN

You have been warned was the anonymous message conveyed to Richard on his belated return to Blanchegarde.

Discussing it with Ambroise who, eyes and ears for any shred of gossip *borne on the wings of the wind*, as Longchamp had written when recalling the King of England with all speed, Richard realised he had not paid sufficient heed to the demands of both Longchamp and his mother. But as he had heard nothing of significance from Hubert Walter, his trusted Bishop of Salisbury who had gone to England to investigate and report to the king how his brother John had been making trouble at home, Richard continued to concentrate every effort in pursuit of his mission abroad.

'This thing —' he threw the message, written in an obviously disguised hand, at Ambroise — 'is patently the effort of one of these Levantine tourists who seeks, on some pretext or other, an audience that he may boast to his friends that he had met the King of England!'

'Sire,' Ambroise was reading the crumpled paper Richard had flung at him, 'if I may make so bold, this is no idle curiosity from some inquisitive tourist who seeks audience with Your Grace, but in my belief, Sire, 'tis an enemy who threatens you. May I take the liberty of suggesting that it may come from one of the allies of Your Highness's brother, Prince John, if not from the King of France?'

'Well,' Richard stretched out his hand for the missive, 'give it to me, that I may read between the lines.'

If he did read between the lines, he still maintained that he saw no necessity to curtail his final advance upon the Holy City and reclaim it for his own.

His readiness to shirk the responsibilities of his kingdom was causing disapproval not only against the king but also growing dislike of his deputy, Chancellor Longchamp. Yet if his Bishop Walter, Richard argued, had thought it necessary to harass him with news of John's mischief, knowing him to be more fool than knave, he would have heard from Walter long before this. In any case, the bishop was due to rejoin him so soon as he had ascertained what had happened in his kingdom...

What had happened in his kingdom during his absence abroad was — John!

Knowing the king to be hundreds of miles away, he had lost no time in seeking to dispose of first Longchamp and then the orderly guidance of the bishop. The opportunity to seize the crown that since his boyhood John had coveted, he thought — in his crafty calculations — to be now within his grasp! He presented his case to his adherents whom he had wooed with hints of royal favours for those who would assist him in the governance of the kingdom, 'so neglected by my brother,' he deplored, 'that he may cover himself with glory in the Holy Land.' For which John cared not a damn, but this he did not mention to the barons and the clerics he beguiled.

All now was set for John to be rid of Longchamp against whom, from the lowest to the highest, he had stirred to the boil in his cauldron of hate.

He circulated among all and sundry how Longchamp had bled the peasants and serfs of their smallest means to increase his own exchequer; how Longchamp, their Chancellor and nominal ruler, had deprived the nobles and lords of the lands of their castles and all their possessions. He told how he himself had also been victimised by the rapacious greed of the hideous cross-eyed hump-backed ape — John was unsparing of epithets in describing the Chancellor's physical and mental disabilities — his own lands and castles having been swallowed in the greedy maw of the king's deputy.

'And what a one,' he lamented, 'for my brother, the king, to have placed in charge of his kingdom! A common scheming odious usurper of our — of *my* royal heritage!'

Apart from this continuous rubbing of salt in the wounds of Longchamp's victims, John had another weapon with which to scourge the king's regent. John's half-brother Geoffrey, bastard son of 'Fair Rosamond', whom the late king had loved more than his own lawful sons, had been created Archbishop of York by his father a week before his death.

John saw in Geoffrey an ally due to an outrage perpetrated by Longchamp's brother-in-law, whom he had made Warden of Dover Castle. Archbishop Geoffrey, returning from a visit to France, had landed at Dover, served Mass in the church and was seized by the minions of the Warden of the Castle. It was evident Longchamp recognised the archbishop as royal, never mind that he knew him to be not only the late king's natural son, but the Chancellor's natural enemy.

Of those whom Longchamp had drained dry of their possessions, even the money and jewels of the Jews he had robbed to enrich his own coffers, John demanded, 'Do you believe he served my brother the king or the Archbishop of York? I tell you that every penny he steals from you and the poorest of the poor he takes to himself and his nepotists!'

At a conference, over which John presided with his satellites, the bishops and clerics — who had suffered from Longchamp's rapacity — unanimously agreed that William Longchamp was unfit to rule over the kingdom. Under command of Prince John, in charge of the 'traitor' and in the king's name, the wretched Chancellor was dragged to the Tower, there to be hanged, drawn and quartered in punishment for one who had so abused the king's trust. (John was ever careful to let all know that the king, as well as himself and lesser subjects, had been betrayed by the monster, William Longchamp.)

But Longchamp was not to be so easily done to death. After a few days of captivity in the Tower he had been hustled off to Canterbury where, with a leniency that John gave out was by order of the king, his brother, he must assume the Cross of Pilgrimage and lay aside his legislation. Thinking, and rightly, that this was only a ruse to be rid of him, either by lifelong imprisonment or — more certainly, by death after undergoing the tortures of the damned on the rack, the rope, and disembowelling while yet alive — Longchamp fled to Dover Castle and placed himself in the care of his sister's husband, the Warden, who got him the disguise of a woman.

One of John's toadies, Hugh Nohant, Bishop of Coventry, reported it strange that he should choose to dress as a woman, whose sex he always professed to hate, and preferred the society of men which, as the bishop discreetly suggested, might have accounted for the king's partiality to ... 'Well, and there it is!'

And there it was.

When Longchamp, in a long gown, hobbled from the castle to the seashore, he sat himself upon a rock to rest. Sighted by a fisherman who mistook him for a wanton, he began to fumble with 'her', and to the horror of Longchamp the gown was pulled open and further exploration discovered...

The fisherman shouted for his mates to come and see. They came and saw, amid roars of laughter and ribald jests at the agonised Chancellor's expense.

The Warden of the castle, hearing the commotion and seeing his brother-in-law in the midst of it, sent servants to his rescue. But they were unable to save the terrified Longchamp from more than immediate assault, for he was captured and taken to prison.

Here, for a week, in solitary confinement he remained, during which time the Warden secretly obtained his release and got him off to Flanders.

On landing in Normandy, Longchamp wrote to the king and to the Pope, giving a full account of his sufferings at the hands of the king's brother, Count Mortain, who, he said, would seize the kingdom if Richard did not return at once to save his crown.

That letter from Longchamp took the better part of two months to reach Richard in Syria, by which time he was almost within sight of Jerusalem.

In this last lap of his pilgrimage Richard had been confronted with manifold hazards. The marriage of his nephew Henry of Champagne to Conrad's widow had been regarded by the French as another grievance to hold against him; but when the Duke of Burgundy, accompanied by Henry, met Richard at Blanchegarde, the French were persuaded that Count Henry and his wife Isabelle would share the royal kingdom of Jerusalem with the English king, and vowed to follow where he led, all doubts of him forgotten.

On 22 of April 1192, when the country burgeoned with blossom and the roads were soft with spring showers to lay the dust, Richard, after some trivial skirmishes with small parties of

Turks between Gaza and Darum, killed a few and took prisoner some half dozen. These were held for the transport of cattle, camels and wagonloads of equipment, since all men available for battle must be used. The next important operation was the capture of Darum which, since the fall of Ascalon, had been the base of Saladin's main supply from Egypt.

At Darum they halted for the festival of Pentecost. All were glad of the respite, especially as the Duke of Burgundy and Henry of Champagne and their renewed forces were reunited with Richard. He gave the Castle of Darum to his nephew as a wedding gift. Then on again, with Richard in the forefront of a formidable host. They encamped at the Canebrake of Starlings.

While they lay here, came more news from England. No letter was this but the Vice-Chancellor, John of Alençon in person. He gave the king a horrifying account of Chancellor Longchamp's flight and capture, with the comic relief of his disguise as a woman and the effect of it on the fisherman. Emphatically he urged the king, 'Sire, it is your duty to come back to your kingdom at once lest you be stripped of your throne, your crown and your subjects. They are dissatisfied that you seem to have neglected your duty to them.'

'I have had all this dinned into me,' said Richard, 'by Longchamp and my mother in every letter they write, but none from my Bishop Hubert. If what you tell be more than gossip spread to stir up trouble, the bishop would have let me know.'

'Your Grace's absence,' doggedly pursued Alençon, 'is the cause of the trouble. Without their king at the head of the realm how can you expect anything but dissension? May I remind Your Grace that your revered father, King Henry, supported the Crusades, but he did not leave his kingdom to a deputy. Your brother the Archbishop of York has also been seriously harassed by —'

'My half-brother,' Richard corrected drily.

'The archbishop,' continued Alençon, 'was attacked while serving Mass, an act of violence reminiscent of the murderous assault upon Thomas Becket, but fortunately with no such disastrous result.'

'Are you trying to tell me that my brother John has a murderous intent against me?'

He realised that what Alençon was conveying could have been induced by John's obsession to reign over the kingdom. But... 'My brother,' said Richard, 'is an overgrown schoolboy. He likes to believe he has the right to his father's throne as his father's favourite son. He was always the spoilt pet of the late king, our father, and also of our old nurse Hodierna.' A smile, half-indulgent, half-regretful, came upon his lips. 'And I admit I too may have spoilt him. It is often the case with a much younger child, the last born of a family. He is either adored or resented by the elder sons and daughters. None, unless it were my mother, had doubts of John. My mother has often said he has a cunning streak in him, besides more than a hint of cruelty. He, unlike the rest of us, has no love for animals. I have seen him as a boy ensnare a bird, tie a cord to its legs and fly it as a kite. I found him at it once and boxed his ears, released the bird, and it flew off to leave John uttering curses at me — how he learned them at that age I do not know — but he swore then to have his revenge on me. It was mere child's play, and that he would seriously seek to injure me now in his manhood or to steal my throne, which is what you came a thousand miles to tell me, is utter nonsense!'

Alençon made a final effort. He was a tall thin man of middle age, his face high-cheekboned and beardless. His eyes, of a sharp pin-pointed grey, narrowed as, undaunted, he persisted, 'Your place, Sire, is in your kingdom. Your duty lies before you

— not *here* —' he waved a hand indicating the green-browed seashore — 'but behind you in the land you have deserted, the land of William of Normandy, the only conqueror since the Romans who has overthrown your precious realm. All of your subjects look to you, their rightful king, to save them from calamitous invasion by an enemy. None who is loyal to Your Grace would wish to see your brother on the throne. I have to tell you,' Alençon looked at him straight, 'it is known not only to me but to the faithful men whom the Bishop of Salisbury employs to investigate any suspicion of malpractice among those of your enemies, that Count John, your brother, intrigues with King Philip of France. He has it well planned, at King Philip's contrivance, that he will lay claim to your rightful realm and also your Angevin Empire, of which he will offer a goodly slice to the King of France. Sire, your subjects look to you to protect and save them from unlawful usurpation of your heritage that you, Sire, have deserted —' again the word was sternly pronounced — 'in order to pursue your Crusade to recover the Holy City from the Muslims...'

Richard, who had listened to this harangue with undisguised impatience, dismissed him abruptly. 'You must be wearied after your journey. My servant will take you to a tent where you may rest.'

Bowing himself out, Alençon withdrew. Richard sank down upon his truckle bed, his head buried in his hands.

One word of Alençon's advocacy rang in his ears like a knell: *Deserted!* Philip! That Philip had deserted his Crusade stabbed him with recurrent reminder. Was he, England's king, to be accused of deserting his kingdom and his people who trusted him? Must his whole life's dream and purpose be shattered by ... desertion? Even as a child at his mother's knee he had sworn to be a faithful servant of Christ. He remembered how her hand had stroked back a curl of his hair that had strayed into his eyes as she had told him: 'Your destiny, my darling, is to serve the Cross. You have two older brothers to serve your father's kingdom should he die...' Yes, even at that young age he had always an urge to fight for and give his life, if need be, to the Cross. He wanted to be a soldier of Christ's army and forget he was the son of a king. He didn't want ever, he would say in shrill temper, to be a king or a king's son! He would be a soldier and go to fight the Saracens.

Henry, his eldest brother, 'the Young King' they called him, was a crusading knight errant, as Richard hoped to be. He had died on one of his adventures; and then there was Geoffrey, who became heir to the throne. He too sickened and died, leaving the boy Arthur. And then John ... When Richard, with the death of those two elder brothers, knew he must be king, John was always saying, even before his childish treble deepened to a harsh distressing croak, that *he* would be a king — the King of England. *That is why, Richard told himself, I named Arthur my heir who, himself only three years old, should have been king when our father died and not I ... Deserted! Am I a deserter? Have I any right to leave my country in danger of ... of whom? John?* The young brother he had always loved, although he knew his faults ... *But what faults are mine to judge him? Far worse than any of John's petty greeds and jealousies. He can beget him a son to follow him, while I ... not even that bastard of the woman whose name I have forgotten. It was none of my begetting ... What is wrong with my manhood? Why have I not taken that girl I married whom I vowed at the altar to love and worship with my body? ... My body that I give to the slaughter of men that I may follow the cause of Christ!*

'God,' he groaned aloud, 'is this my punishment, to lose my kingdom and see it laid waste by John who has no notion how to govern? But have *I*?'

If only his Bishop Walter had come to him instead of that pompous ass. Alençon … A chuckle followed the groan as he recalled how Longchamp, according to Alençon, when mistaken for a woman disguised in a gown had been all but raped! Yes, Longchamp whom he trusted to have so deceived him, plundered his treasury, taxed the impoverished, and taken to himself the lands and monies that should have enriched the king's coffers to endow those in need of his bounty…

Have I none whom I can trust? he cried within him. *Is human nature so unworthy? What is truth, as Pontius Pilate asked? What is God? Where the Holy Cross of Christ that I have sworn to follow?* 'A senseless piece of wood' as Saladin had called it!

His hands left his face; he fell on his knees and prayed. 'O, Mother of God, have pity on me, a sinner. Intercede with your Precious Son that I may be guided as to what I am to do … Am I to forsake my cause to recover the Holy Sepulchre from the Unbelievers? Turn my back upon your Holy City and leave my followers to complete my Crusade? A deserter! Am I to save my earthly kingdom and lose Your Kingdom of Eternal Life?

He was roused from his prayers by a step outside the tent and a sound of weeping. A voice sob-choked, 'The king, my king!'

Rising from his knees he called, 'Who is it? What do you want of me?'

The guard at the tent allowed the king's chaplain, William of Poitiers, to pass in.

'Sire, my son!' He dashed a hand across his tear-washed eyes. 'It has come to me, to all of us who serve you, that your Vice-Chancellor has brought you news to make imperative your return to England. Do you agree to go back with him?'

'No!' Richard loudly denied it. 'I agree to no such thing. I will debate with myself and my God what I should do. I am in sore distress, Father. Will you not advise me? You come, I think, in answer to my prayer. What you advise so will I follow.'

'Then, my son,' the priest took his hand and bowed his lips upon it, 'I implore you, my king, in the name of God, that you will not renounce your Holy Mission for any reason, not even your duty to your kingdom. You have *no* duty but to God, who has chosen you to perform His Will that you save the Holy City for the Christians, now and hereafter. Remember how God made you the conqueror of Cyprus where none has hitherto rightfully succeeded. Remember how God has entrusted his Holy Land to you — that you *alone* may save it from destruction now that King Philip, your ally, has deserted the Cause he pledged to fulfil. And will you also desert the mission that you —'

'Don't!' cried Richard. 'Don't *you* accuse me of desertion! I would as soon desert my faith in God's eternal love as desert my mission and forsake my pledge! I am God's Anointed and have been chosen by Him to reign over a kingdom that, against my will, I have inherited.'

'You have inherited no kingdom, my son, save that of God. Can you not see how you are favoured by His Almighty Will? Have you forgotten His words to His Father when he wept tears of blood to know that he must die in torture on the Cross? ... "Thy Will, not mine, be done," He said ... It is His Will, from the day you left the Western world to follow the Cross, that your enemies have cause to fear you. Remember how the Sultan Saladin, Almighty in *his* world, fears you as greater than himself, for he knows you to be the champion of the Christ he denies. It you desert this Third Crusade, you endanger the Holy City and the Cross you have sworn to save, and suffer the ruthless desecration of the Muslims. Would you be named Richard, the Deserter, you of the Lion Heart?'

Richard stood in silence, his head bowed, to hear the priest's voice again repeat that word to break him: *Deserter!*

Then: 'Father...' He knelt. 'You have saved me. You are sent by God in answer to my prayer for guidance that I may know where my duty lies ... I will order my herald to proclaim throughout the army that all men must prepare to follow me. From this day forth we go straightway to Jerusalem!'

Berengaria and Joan were still at Acre. The transport that Joan had hoped would take them back to France and England was not yet commandeered for their departure. Every galley, the captain of the fleet informed her, had been bespoken by the king for reinforcements.

'That, of course,' grumbled Berengaria, 'might have been expected. Richard only cares for his army. I — we — don't count. I must stay here in these miserable conditions, eaten alive by mosquitoes. At home we have slaves to fan them away and cover me and my bed with veils to keep them off...'

'Will you never have done complaining?' cried Joan. Her fury against Richard for daring to negotiate a marriage between herself and the Sultan's brother had cooled. She realised, as he had told her, that he never intended any such impossible alliance. He had only made the suggestion so that Saladin might see it as preliminary to a truce. That Richard had not paid them a visit while pursuing his campaign within barely half a day's ride from Acre, was for Berengaria another source of grievance.

She sat at the window in the castle that overlooked the town, where crowds of natives swarmed in the bazaar amid a continuous uproar from sellers at the stalls offering their wares.

The windows here, as in most of the castles in Europe, had no glass and gave no protection from the noise below. 'And what with the heat,' lamented Berengaria, 'and the revolting food of these heathens, wonder it is we aren't dead! We ought never to have joined Richard after Cyprus.'

She turned from the window to scoop up in her arms a kitten playing in the rushes. One of the servants had found it astray in the debris of the city. She cuddled the kitten close to her. 'It's all very well for you — poor little thing, you were born here and you don't mind the heat, nor the food, so long as you can stomach the stinking muck they give you. And why,' to Joan who was seated at a tambour frame embroidering a width of tapestry, 'why, if you can't get transport, don't you insist that Richard sends one of his ships for us? You give in to him in everything, and if you can't get transport then I *will;* I'll send word to my father to find me a ship to take me — never mind *you* — back to Navarre. I wish I had never left my own country and my own people. What misery it is here since the fall of Acre ... I want to go home!'

'Oh, for God's sake!' Joan stabbed her needle with force into the tapestry as if at her sister queen's face. 'I'm sick to death of your moanings. *Send* to your father, then, to take you home. Do you think *I* like to be cooped up in this hateful place?'

Her patience, with which for weeks she had submitted to Berengaria's laments, had worn down. She had more than enough to worry her, she told herself, without these incessant wailings ...

Messages brought to Joan by her courier told of her brother's determined advance upon Jerusalem. Alençon had called on her at Acre on his way back from his interview with Richard. He told her of the troubling conditions in England and how John had determined to seize the throne by hook or by crook. 'If the king,' Alençon had said, 'insists on continuing his Crusade to the capture of Jerusalem which will take him into August, providing he obtains the equipment he requires for the utter defeat of Saladin's forces, England may be faced with civil war ... If the king's brother lacks land,' he made a clumsy joke, 'he lacks no followers.'

So that's it, thought Joan. *If John is hand-in-glove with Philip, heaven knows what they will plot together! Richard has always been blind to John's treachery and cunning. He ought to go back and see for himself what is happening there, before it's too late!*

Meantime Richard was more than ever concerned with what was happening here, while he waited for shipments to bring reinforcements to the nearest port. These he greatly needed if he were to outnumber Saladin's formidable hosts ranged along the route he had mapped for himself.

A report from the hill of Montjoie, so named by the previous Crusade of 1187 because from there a far distant glimpse of Jerusalem had been seen, gave him some uneasiness when a scout returned with the news of a Turkish ambush waiting to strike at the Christian force.

At this Richard delayed no more, but was in his saddle at dawn. Summoning a company of knights, he managed to surprise the ambushing Turks in the valley below the hills of Gideon. Helter-skelter they fled before Richard's dreaded battle axe as hard on their horses' heels he, in the forefront of his knights, captured three camels and half a dozen of their best horses and mules carrying food, spices and silks.

'And what would they want with silks?' Richard asked his sweating knights as they rested after that heated skirmish with the sun high in heaven, and no sign of water in the desolate outlook before them of desert sand and rocks; no herbage for their beasts to graze, no water to quench their thirst. 'Do they think to deck their dancing girls in silks out here in the wilds? I should have thought they preferred them decked in nothing,' laughed Richard.

'I am told,' remarked Ambroise, ever near at hand with his tablets, 'that the Turks always bring with them their wives or harlots to pass the time.'

'Their time,' Richard said, 'is not our time, and no time now for our further advance. Look!'

With some of his knights he had climbed to a hill top. There, within the stretch of desert waste, the hills high above Judea slid away to slopes of verdant green interspersed with the dark heavy grey of rocks; beyond in the distance was a shining glimpse of sea. Then, in the brazen light of the early sun, it seemed as if heaven had opened to pour gold upon a mirage of domes and towers, and on fairy-like minarets of ivory caught in a shimmer of topaz light that faded as he watched...

'Too far, too far,' he murmured. And to his knights: 'To advance farther in this waste land would be courting disaster without sufficient arms and men. Saladin has more reinforcements just arrived which will greatly outnumber ours, even if our convoys could reach Jaffa without meeting the Saracen galleys. So,' he lowered his head, 'we turn back ... I say *no*!'

This to Robert de Brugers, a Hospitaller and one of his most valiant knights who besought him: 'Sire, I beg you to go on. We can be a match for any of Saladin's heathens!'

'No!' roared Richard again. 'I have seen heaven and I —' His voice broke. He lifted his shield to cover his face and cried aloud for all to hear the words that came to them in harsh crescendo.

'God! My God! I cannot look upon the Holy City if it is Your Will that I may not deliver it out of the hands of Your enemies ... or let me die!'

Against all opposition from his Templars and Hospitallers, who implored Richard not to retreat but to make the forty-odd miles to their goal, he determined to fight his way back to Ascalon, there to wait until his army had been sufficiently equipped to go forward and take Cairo (the Babylon of the Bible) and Beirut or Damascus.

It was now well into June, and the heat in the torrid summer of the Middle East became intolerable to the northerners in their heavy coats of mail. But they struggled on behind their king. He, impervious to climatic conditions, led them mounted on his gallant Fauvel who, like his master, cared nothing for the heat. Under his visor Richard's eyes were almost blinded by the sweat that dripped from his forehead; and not until he raised his visor to wipe his face did he see the advance of a large convoy come from Jaffa with some of his much-needed equipment.

Joyfully he called to his followers, 'See! We shall now have arms enough with which to meet an attack!'

Too late: a strong cavalry of Saracens with their howling cries of 'Allah! Allah-ooh!' had swooped down upon the convoy. They cut through the advancing Christian ranks, scything with their spears and vicious scimitars at Richard's cavalry and foot soldiers in a wholesale massacre. While greatly outnumbered, the king and his troops fought wildly; many of his knights were unhorsed, but Richard on his charger managed to escape, and succeeded in slicing off the heads and limbs of several Turks. His dreaded battle axe had never served him better. Yet, even though utter defeat appeared to be imminent, the Christian army, inspired by their king, fought on and he, together with the Earl of Leicester and the leader of the convoy, put the Turks to flight; but not before the field was strewn with the bodies of dead and dying Christians, and the torn limbs and corpses of the Turks.

The loss of so many of his knights either killed or taken prisoner further to deplete his armies was a bitter blow to Richard. But, again deaf to the entreaties of his Templars to defy Saladin's repeated attacks and to push on to the Holy City, he remained adamant. It would bring disaster to the Crusade, he argued, were he now to attempt the siege of Jerusalem still with insufficient men and arms and in the height of summer.

To Saladin's armies the heat was no deterrent, they were born to it; even their armour was of the lightest, worn under thin linen surtouts; and they were adept in the use of their murderous weapons, the curved scimitars and the cruel poisoned spear and arrow heads,

'We do not use poisoned weapons,' Richard said; 'and to advance now would discredit not only me, your leader, but this, the third Crusade. I am well aware,' he told them, 'that there are those in England and France who would rejoice to see me and my Crusade defeated, but I'll not give them that satisfaction. I will bide my time until I know I can satisfy myself and my God!'

However, seeing they were still undecided, he said that if the Military Orders would make a decision with five of the Templars, five Hospitallers and five barons of France, he would be prepared to besiege Jerusalem — but, he stressed, '*Not* as your leader of the attack, nor as your general in command of the army. I will go only as leader of my own selected men, and you others can do your best — or your worst!'

A majority vote from the Templars and Hospitallers not to proceed to Jerusalem until the king gave the word, and never without him as leader, was passed. The French, however, led by the Duke of Burgundy, were determined to advance to the Holy City. While still debating with the French, Richard's scouts — all picked men who could speak and understand Arabic — arrived with news of a vast Saracen caravan approaching from Egypt.

Richard at once saw the advantage of making an attack on the caravan and seizing the booty, for he believed the Saracens would not have with them a force that could offer a strong enough resistance. 'If we can seize the booty,' he told his knights, 'it will be divided among you all, and a third to the French.' (This an obvious bribe to Burgundy, who had been the most hostile of the French against Richard's interim retreat.) 'We will then proceed to Cairo with the rich supply afforded by the caravan — I know what Saladin's caravans can offer! He is not so lean-pursed as am I. We can then wait for a well-timed opportunity to pursue the advance on Jerusalem. I prefer this to be in the autumn, for then we shall not be tormented by the heat and these godon flies!' All of them had suffered from a plague of flies and mosquito bites.

Disagreements and opposition from the French were now overcome with the promise of a share in Saladin's vast supplies. Richard, attended by five hundred knights and a thousand men-at-arms, set out with Burgundy and his French behind him, to intercept the caravan.

According to Ambroise the king rode forth *under the splendour of the moon*. Out of consideration for his troops Richard preferred to travel at night and avoid the heat of the day. But Saladin, whose scouts were ever on the watch, had been informed of the English king's latest venture, and he sent five hundred picked men commanded by Aslam, one of his most distinguished emirs, to divert the Egyptian caravan from its course for a route unknown to the Christians.

Besides those escorting the caravan, Aslam had mustered an army of more than two thousand horsemen and foot soldiers. When Richard heard of this diversion, which would entail much delay in overtaking Aslam and his forces in an unknown and uncharted mountain course, he sent a scout to discover if it were possible to waylay the caravan before Aslam had gone too far to intercept it. The report was encouraging: the caravan had halted at a site called in Arabic the Waters of Kuweilfeh, translated as the Round Cistern. It would be a good place for Aslam's army to rest and water their horses.

A native Syrian scout in the service of Richard came up with the advice that, if the king hastened, he would show him a short cut of which he knew and had often followed when tending his herd of goats. The king, Malek Ric, could then find the caravan before dawn while the army still slept. For the Syrian assured Richard that none of the camp would wake before morning. He had ascertained, disguised as a Bedouin, that the Emir Aslam would never believe the Christians could follow his Saracens across those mountain passes.

Aslam had not reckoned with Richard's well-organised espionage, nor that the king himself would conduct a reconnaissance to prove the truth of the Syrian's report. Also disguised as a Bedouin, indistinguishable from a genuine Arab, his hair and face covered, Richard climbed the steep ascent to the Round Cistern, a wide pool sunk in the level of a rocky mountain peak. As the Syrian had told him, he found the camp asleep, his secret approach unseen and unheard; their deep snores implied that they and their emir had liberally sampled the bounteous stores of food and wine from the caravan.

Back went Richard to his army. Night had faded, and the rose-fingered dawn heralded the rising sun that stained the sky above the mountains as if the heavens wept blood. Richard crossed himself. Was it a good or bad omen? He remembered an old adage translated to him from the English: *Red sky at dawning, shepherd's warning* ... He too was a shepherd, herding his flock to follow, or be driven before him.

Then, cheered by the sight of his own camp awaiting his return to give him shouts of welcome, he hailed them joyfully. 'All's well! We can fall upon them while they sleep. From their snores I can guess *why* they sleep so sound! We will be up with the sun before they wake if we start now.'

But one of Aslam's scouts had also been on the prowl and, disguised in a coat of mail stolen from a dead Templar, he alerted the Muslim camp. Richard, who had been prepared for this, gave Aslam little time to assemble his men, yet time enough for them to rain showers of arrows at the advancing Christians. This affected them no more than a downpour of hailstones. Richard, with his heavily armed knights behind him, charged the Muslims. Unprepared for so fierce an attack they took to headlong flight, *as hare before hounds* as described by Bohardin, who was strictly more accurate than Ambroise since he was neither troubadour nor sentimentalist. 'So many of our men,' he says, 'reputed to be the bravest sought to save their lives on the fleetest of our horses...' By which we may assume that the Saracen foot soldiers were the worst sufferers, mown down by the Christian cavalry and unable to defend themselves.

The wood of Richard's lance used alternately with his battle axe became sodden with blood... This from Ambroise, who may have heard tell of it, for he had no active part in the appalling destruction of the Turks.

Saladin's routed forces took refuge in the hills; but while Richard's soldiers were looting the caravan and the knights dealing their deadly assault on all those near enough to fall under the forest of lances, Emir Aslam, who had ordered a retreat, charged forward with a company of horsemen in attempt to prevent the total despoilment of the Egyptian caravan. He was met by the Earl of Leicester laying about him right and left. The emir, wounded but not too severely, urged his Muslims to stand firm in their defence. In vain: they were overcome, and again forced to retreat with the few survivors of the slaughter. The ground, thick with the bodies of the slain, made it almost impossible for the Christian cavalry to advance without their horses trampling on dead and dying.

It was a holocaust, with the fleeing Muslims calling on Allah to have mercy, the shrieks and groans of the dying men's horses and camels, the thunder of hooves as the cavalry pursued their charge, the air glittering with sparks from swords and lances, and everywhere the reek of blood. *Hands, arms, legs, even the eyes of the Turks bestrewed the earth,* according to Ambroise, who evidently enjoyed piling on the agony from hearsay or his safe vantage point where the soldiers were busy collecting the caravan's booty.

Thirteen hundred Turkish horsemen were killed not counting the foot soldiers … The caravan yielded besides four thousand camels. Again an exaggeration from Ambroise which may be whittled down to no more than a hundred or so camels, yet there was no denying the booty did include pack-camels laden with loot from Baghdad: gold, silver, jewels, various textiles, arms of every kind, tents, hides, water bottles of leather, sacks of barley, wheat, flour — enough to feed the entire Christian army on the march.

The Battle of the Round Cistern was for Richard a major victory, for Saladin a major disaster. Now he was certain that the Christians would go straight ahead for Jerusalem. The walls of the city were reinforced. Saladin would take no risks: every approach must be defended, even to destruction of the wells that the enemy should have no water; the springs must be dammed and poisoned, that should any water escape it would kill the thirst-stricken Christians.

But still the Crusade, headed by Malek Ric, the English king, did not advance. Had he retreated and given up his mission? Saladin, pacing his tent in feverish anxiety, sent for Bohardin to report. 'What would be the next move of this unpredictable King Richard of the Lion Heart — or of a tiger's heart, more like?' was Saladin's lugubrious query. 'He knows no mercy. He slays with the savagery of the most bloodthirsty man-eating beast from the jungle...'

While Saladin prayed in the mosque, calling upon Allah and the Prophet to advise him whether he should defend Jerusalem or evacuate it before Malek Ric, the Tiger, should fall upon and destroy what they dared to call their 'Holy City', Richard was again confronted with dissension and revolt, in particular from Hugh, Duke of Burgundy.

Notwithstanding that all the Crusaders — French, German, English — rejoiced at the victory of the Round Cistern, the French were determined, as Richard was not, to advance without delay upon Jerusalem. There began a renewal of the arguments between Richard's followers and those of Hugh, Duke of Burgundy, representing the King of France who had left him in command of his army.

The hostility of Burgundy towards Richard was at its height when he exploited his hatred and jealousy of the intrepid English king in a lewd, revolting song sung by his men in which Richard's sexual propensities were emphasised. Richard's reply, in similar terms, dwelt upon Burgundy's lecherous womanising and did nothing to restore a pretence of amity between them. Instead it brought matters to a head. Richard insisted that arbitration must settle the dispute. Whatever the verdict of the umpires of whom he appointed a dozen chosen from his own and Burgundy's knights, their decision would allow of no appeal.

News of this, when brought to Saladin by Bohardin, gave the Sultan to hope that the umpires would declare against the English king's advance upon their 'Holy City'. He waited in agonised impatience for the verdict.

Richard, no less anxious while the arbitration went on and interminably on, was driven to consult an oracle, or rather a hermit supposedly to be possessed of clairvoyance. He lived in a cave on the Mountain of Joy (Montjoie), from where Richard had gazed upon a vision of Jerusalem, and covered his eyes that they should not look upon the city of his dreams if he were not to be entrusted to deliver it from the heathens.

When, for a second time, he reached the Joyful Mountain with some of his knights, and Ambroise as ever in attendance, they were inclined to doubt the authenticity of the so-called prophet at sight of the strange apparition emerging from the entrance to the cave. He looked more like an ape than a man. Stark naked, his body was covered with a mat of hair that hung from his head almost down to his feet.

'You, the king,' he said to Richard, amazing them all by speaking in cultured Norman French. 'Enter. I bid you welcome.'

He led them to the interior of the dark and noisome cave, and into a kind of oratory or chapel carved from the rocky wall. Opening a cavity concealed by a curtain of rushes, he drew forth a wooden cross. 'This,' he told them, 'was made from the Tree at Calvary. It still bears the traces of the precious blood of our tortured Lord.'

All stood with heads bowed in reverence; the more credulous knelt, praying forgiveness for having doubted the prophet. Only Richard, who had come there in full belief of the hermit's authenticity, was disposed to have more evidence. On other occasions he had been offered by mendicants pieces of wood purporting to be relics of the True Cross of Calvary; and the shocking appearance of the oracular hermit did nothing to alter his disbelief in him or 'the useless piece of wood' despised by Saladin.

'Ask,' demanded the prophet in a hollow voice that echoed through the rocky walls, 'and it shall be answered as the Lord God decides.'

'Then — do I proceed towards Jerusalem now,' Richard asked, 'or do I wait until it is ordained that I pass through the gates of the Holy City?'

The hermit shook his head. A groaning sigh rose up as if torn from his entrails. 'No!' Like a hammer blow the word repeated to echo through the walls of rock. 'No! *You* will not, this time nor any time, enter through the Holy Gates. Your task is done. You are undefeated but the City is not for you — although you, of the Third Crusade, are the victor. I foretell this as I foretell my own death, which will occur a week from today. I have seven days to make my peace with God, as it is written.' And again the hollow voice rang out, that again seemed to echo from those cavernous walls of rock: '...*as it is written*...' and fading, sank.

The kneeling knights signed themselves; none now doubted the truth of the oracle. Not so Richard; or maybe he wished to disbelieve. Had the oracle spoken otherwise, he might not have hesitated but at once pursued his advance upon Jerusalem and so completed his mission. Yet he must be sure.

'I wish you,' said the king, 'to return with me to my camp.'

The knights rose from their knees. Ambroise was in a state, the oracle in a stare.

'You doubt my word? The Word of God?'

'I want,' Richard said, 'to hear the truth.'

Ambroise devoutly hoped he would *not* hear the truth if it meant another awful march across these mountains, dying of thirst, bitten by flies and his mouth full of dust.

'Get yourself clothed,' commanded Richard. 'If you have anything to cover you.'

To the dismay of the camp they saw, led on a halter by the king on his horse, what they took to be a wild beast. His hairy hide had only been sparsely covered in rags taken from a heap that was the hermit's bed.

In an isolated tent at the camp, food had been placed within his reach, and a strict observance kept on him that none should interfere with his devotions. He passed each day, and possibly each night, upon his knees clutching his holy relic. The drone of his unintelligible jargon might have been Hebrew, French, Hindustani or mere gibberish to Richard when he crept on silent feet to listen.

There on his knees, in solitary confinement, the hermit remained for one full week, and on the seventh day, as prophesied, he died.

EIGHT

'The Oracle has spoken!' said Richard, looking down upon the body of the hermit. They had dressed him in the robes of a priest and had him carried to his cave, where Richard ordered a grave to be prepared for him. This at the hermit's own request and with his last words, the only words — other than his prayers — that had passed his lips since they brought him to the camp to die.

He was given Extreme Unction, and Richard, with four of his knights — and, of course, Ambroise, scribbling on his tablets everything he saw and heard (and much that he had not seen or heard) — attended the last of him. Richard returned to camp and announced his intention of leaving the Holy Land. 'I who give orders must take orders from the Highest Source. The hermit was endowed with the sight to see, the ears to hear. I must obey.'

Consternation fell upon his followers. Had he lost interest in his Holy Mission?

'But first,' Richard continued, ignoring the chorus of voices raised in protest, 'I must make my peace with Saladin.'

Leicester and some others clamoured, 'Sire, we beseech you — do not abandon us for your return to England! It is barely forty more miles to the Gates.'

'Never fear,' he assured them. 'I will come back to be with you when you have done what I — God forgive me — have left undone, until I can kneel with you at the foot of the Holy Sepulchre. As you know, I am continuously harassed by urgent demands from my bishops and my good friend Hubert Walter, not to fail my duty to my earthly kingdom even while I serve my heavenly kingdom. Do not believe that I am defeated in my mission. I am still in possession of the coast of Palestine, and my nephew, Henry of Champagne, my sister's son is, with his wife, King Elect of Jerusalem — but only until I claim my right to the Holy City, when I will return!'

Whether he had or had not convinced them of his good intent to fulfil his ultimate goal, he left them none the less eager to advance on the last lap of the journey even without him. And when the discussions regarding his determination to return to England subsided, he promised to leave with them his plan of action. There would be an abundance of food and equipment for the next advance, thanks to the capture of the Egyptian caravan. If they waited until the cool of the autumn it would not take more than a day and a night to reach Jerusalem. Meantime he would have come to peace with Saladin so there would be no hindrance to hold them back from the Holy City…

They saw his point. Yes! To make peace with Saladin would mean they had won the war! So they hopefully thought, as did Richard when he began negotiations with Saladin. He pondered over his letter to the Sultan, writing and rewriting it half a dozen times to be translated into Turkish by the Syrian scout, who understood and spoke some English.

But Henry of Champagne, whose head had swelled in anticipation of the crown he would wear as King Elect of Jerusalem, got in first. With unexampled arrogance he took upon himself to write dictatorially to the Sultan: *I demand, in the name of the King of England who has given me all the towns along the coast…*

'God damn his soul!' roared Richard when he read a copy of this letter from Henry. 'I never gave him the Palestine coast!

See —' he thrust the English translation of the letter under the nose of Leicester, who had brought it to him — 'see what the impudent young rascal dares to write! *And I demand* — he demands!' shouted Richard. 'I'll have the hide off his back for this!'

'That you deliver to me,' continued Henry while Richard spluttered indignant threats of violence to his nephew, who may have deserved all he didn't get from his irate uncle, *'all the other towns that I may make my peace with you...'*

If Richard were furious when he read what the 'impudent young rascal' had dared to write, Saladin on receiving it was almost apoplectic. He raved. He tore his hair. He bit the cushions of the divan on which he lay when the letter was delivered by a trembling messenger.

'You —!' Saladin pointed a shaking finger at the pale courier who was kneeling, head bowed, in fear of the Sultan. 'Stand, you! Stand up!' He snatched a scimitar beside him on the divan. 'Cur! I myself will cut off your head!'

It was just at this moment that another messenger arrived, this time from Richard. The jewel-hilted scimitar was suspended in mid-air above the bowed head of the half-fainting bearer of the letter that looked to be his death sentence. Saladin paused. He dropped the scimitar, and to the bowing Syrian who brought the message from the English king he rapped out, 'What now?'

It was a conciliatory letter from Richard, expressing his affection for his Illustrious Friend, Yusuf Salah-ed-Din ibn Ayjub (to give him his full title), that in view of his nephew Count Henry's unpardonable audacity in taking upon himself the right of the King of England, he had no wish to play the Pharaoh in this land. He went on to assure his *Honourable Friend* that *your Mussulmen shall not perish nor will my Franks from any untoward disagreements between us...* There was a good deal more of it to the effect that he apologised for his nephew Henry of Champagne, his sister's son, for his unprecedented authority *for which I, the king, have given him no warrant whatsoever to assume...*

Having put Henry in possession of certain of the Sultan's countries, Richard went on to withdraw them and placed his nephew at the disposal of Saladin: *wherever you command him to accompany you he will obey ... As to what displeased you in my former communications with Malek El Adil (Saphadin) I renounced them all.* Then came a mild stipulation: *If you will allow me but a farm or a village I will accept it and grant you the equivalent.*

'There's the cunning devil he is!' exclaimed Bohardin, to whom Saladin had passed the letter for his opinion. 'To gain his ends he softens you with honeyed words and sticks a knife in your back, for while he knows we have the upper hand he offers himself to you in humble servility. I beseech you, All Highest, not to be deceived by his subtle cunning. Allah alone is your protection against this dangerous man who has the deadly bite of a serpent!'

'How right you are!' nervously agreed Saladin, his face turning a greenish lemon as he listened to Bohardin, whose word he never doubted. 'I have always,' the Sultan admitted, 'looked upon the English king as a man of honour and a bold and courageous opponent. I now perceive I must be on my guard and play the same cunning game as he. I suppose him to be a good hand at chess. I would like to meet him in a game.'

'It would be a great game between you and King Richard,' replied Bohardin, 'and who can tell which one would be checkmate?'

'I have no doubt,' said Saladin proudly, 'which one of us would be checkmate. Am I not the champion of all chess players in Islam? But since the king writes to me as a friend I will answer him in his manner. Take down this letter...'

So, in due course, Richard received an equally conciliatory reply assuring him that the Sultan would regard the nephew of the English king as one of his own sons. 'Henry won't thank him for that!' chuckled Richard. *And to you, O King,* Saladin sweetly informed him, *I will grant the greatest of all your churches throughout my empire, the Church of the Resurrection of your God, His son...*

The rest of the countries he already held he would keep, and those along the sea coast he would divide between King Richard and himself. But as for Ascalon ... To this he added what might have been an apologia. *Until now, that to which I objected was the fall of Ascalon...* As to the villages for which the king asked, Saladin implied that so far as he was concerned he cared nothing for them, but if his Mussulmen refused to yield them to the King of England, he would offer him the town of Lydda in exchange for Ascalon (a pawn of no importance to him, as Malek Ric well knew).

At once Richard moved a defiant knight on the chequerboard of diplomatic relations: *It is impossible for me to concede one stone of Ascalon's fortifications, fallen though they be. I intend to rebuild your 'Bride of Syria'.*

After this, negotiations came to a halt. Richard sent three hundred of his Templars and Hospitallers to transfer the garrison of Darum to Ascalon. With the rest of his army he went on to Acre. From there he would embark for Jaffa, thence to Europe; but first he must make his peace with Berengaria, whom he had not seen nor communicated with for several months.

After having been warmly welcomed by his sister, he sought Berengaria in her apartment. He found her alone, seated in the aperture of the window plucking a doleful tune on the strings of a lute.

No warmth was in the startled look she gave him at his entrance, nor did his disbelieved travel-stained appearance — he had not waited to change his clothes before presenting himself — lessen the acrimonious reception she offered to her errant husband. 'I wonder,' she told him, without rising from her seat, and with her fingers still straying on the lute strings, 'that you deign to visit me, having for so long forgotten my existence.'

'My absence is none of my choosing, nor of my choice is war. I am not my own master.'

He made as if to embrace her. She laid aside her lute and slid under his outstretched arms.

'You have not written one word to me all this long time, yet every so often you send a letter to Joan. One of your messengers brought her a box of that sticky jelly stuff which she couldn't eat — said it was too sickly. She gave it to her page, but there was nothing for me.'

'Why, damme,' he protested. 'They were meant for you, not my sister. The courier must have mistaken for whom they were intended.'

'A likely tale!' she flashed. 'I loathe the "delight" of the Turks. And why is your absence none of your choosing, when everyone knows you choose only and care for nothing but war to chase the Infidels out of their country? And when you catch them, you kill them and tread on them as if they were beetles!' Then, from a safe distance as again he came to her, 'And why,' she repeated, 'is war not of your choosing? You say you are not your own master.'

'I am not. I serve a Master higher than myself. And *why*,' he asked, his eyebrows comically raised, 'do you look at me as if I were an undesirable?'

'Because you are,' she retorted, 'undesirable to me.'

'My dear child —' he began. She took him up sharply on that.

'I am not your dear, nor your child. I am a queen. *Your* queen, whom you have abandoned!' She spoke in her mixture of broken French and Spanish, having the blood not only of France but of Spain in her veins from her Castilian mother.

He had always found her Norman French endearing in the past, and herself no less endearing in the present, with her assumption of her regal state that sat oddly on her adolescence. 'Presumably a virgin,' as was cattily said of her by de Born or one of his favourites when the Queen Mother had brought her to him as his future bride. It was her seemingly virginal youth that had attracted him from the first. He had never been physically desirous of the flamboyant overblown femininity of the Angevin women.

'And,' the young voice continued in rising persistence, 'you dare to come to me without changing your travel clothes. Covered in dust and dirt — ugh!' She shuddered. 'I do not like you near me. I will send for a servant to attend you.'

'So will you!' In two strides he had caught and lifted her up to the level of his face, flushed with the sudden heat of desire. 'None shall attend me but you who has the right — as I demand — and want you!'

He lowered his mouth to hers. She screamed, shrank from him and clawed at him. 'Oh, you brute — beast — you great hairy beast! I hate you! Leave me — go!'

At that he turned on his heel, and without another word or backward look he went. As for her, she could have bitten out her tongue rather than have spoken as she did in her temper, that when roused almost matched his own. Nor, in her heart, did she wish to be rid of him, as her wrathful dismissal would seem to confirm. *After all,* she admitted, *he is my husband...*

Not that she would have asked for husband such as he. She would have preferred a younger man, one nearer her own age and who would tell her how pretty she was, as her cousin Philippe used to say, and that when she was older she would set all men aflame for her. And now she was married ... not that marriage would make any difference to her when she remembered how, at her father's Court, she had heard that almost every wife had a lover or lovers. And then there was that young Scot, red-haired like Richard, with an outlandish name. He had been knighted by the king for his courage in killing single-handed three Turks. Where was he now, that Scot with his strange way of speaking either English or French? *And why,* she asked herself, not for the first time, *if this is a Crusade in the service of God, why should it be an honour to kill — for God? Surely He who bade us love one another should disapprove of what is nothing short of murder...*

Returning to the window seat she took up her lute again, thinking: *All these Crusaders, and Richard their leader, are Christians, and yet they keep on killing, killing, killing! Any Saracen or Turk who believes in the Prophet — Mahomet, is it? And their God Allah, they kill in return all who believe in God and his Son Jesus! How can one say either belief is right? No, I must not say such things. I am a sinner. It is the devil who is making me think so wickedly. I'll to the priest and confess...*

Having got thus far in her meditations she began plucking again the strings of her lute, her conscience salved by her decision to confess, if necessary. She always rather avoided confession, for the priest — one of the king's chaplains —

would give such severe penances, even to the scourging of her naked body, which she must never look upon since it was the discovering of their nakedness that had brought about the fall of man — and woman. 'And I suppose,' she said in a singsong to her lute, 'that it is a sin to look upon a naked statue — but why? If animals don't have to clothe themselves, why should — Yes? who is it?'

Her tuneless song broke off abruptly as the curtains parted and a voice enquired, 'Your Highness, may I…?'

'Enter, then,' she said to Blondel, the young minstrel whom Richard had left at Acre to entertain his wife and sister with his songs and music.

'Would Your Grace,' he asked, bowing before her, 'wish me to play the song the king wrote in verse and which I have set to music?'

She smiled at him. A pretty youth, she thought, and prettier in contrast to the untidy uncouth appearance of the king, who had come to her without even washing his face! 'Yes, play to me,' she said. 'You play so well.'

He had brought his recorder, and lowering himself cross-legged on the rugs that were part of the spoils looted by the Christians at the fall of Acre, he played a charming roundelay and then sang in his Norman French the words of it, which he had written in anticipation of the king's return to England.

Dieu est venue avec sa Puissance
Bientot en ira le roi d'Angleterre.

While Blondel was fulfilling his king's command to entertain his queen, Richard, having relieved himself of his anger against his wife — 'that impudent young devil, to come at me like a wild cat!' — he sought his bedchamber.

When his servant had removed his filthy clothes and dressed him in a silken night shift, he was thankful for the comfort of a bed after sleeping upon straw or sacking, for though fastidious as a woman when in his palaces or castle, he lived as did his soldiers in the conditions of war, with no discrimination permitted by him for his rank.

So soon as his head touched the pillow he was asleep, and would have slept the clock round had he not been awakened by a commotion in the street below and an ear-splitting trumpet call. He raised his head even as his door was flung open and one of his knights unceremoniously shouted, 'Sire, wake! The Saracens are at Jaffa! Get up! Saladin will have seized the citadel unless we come to the rescue in time.'

Hardly waiting for the knight to finish speaking, Richard was out of bed. 'My armour! Give me my armour!' And before his servant could bring it he seized it from Augustin of London, the English knight who had burst in upon him with this latest news. Dragging his coat of mail over his night shirt and ramming on his helmet, he was out of the room like a rocket. Calling to arms all the men he could muster, and with some Pisans and Genoese, he set off for the relief of Jaffa.

He and his knights went by sea, thinking it to be the quicker course, while the rest of his army took to the road, and fifty galleys followed them. Unfortunately Richard had mistaken the weather that had been calm, but as they neared Mount Carmel contrary winds held up his ships. Not until three days later was the king's leading galley, its red sails emblazoned with the three leopards of England, sighted by those on the watch for him at Jaffa.

The garrison was already about to surrender when renewed hope at the sight of the king and his ship gave them to hold on. But it seemed that Richard's luck was out. His fleet had not yet caught up with him while he waited beyond the harbour, for he could not venture to storm the citadel against Saladin's vast forces without his ships to bombard from the shore, with his army still on the march to overtake him.

Frantically he cried to God, 'For Your sake, why do You keep me waiting when I am on Your service?' In his frenzy he blasphemed God, himself, his mission and his laggard fleet. 'Why in hell don't they come?' he cried to his shocked knights. 'Why am I kept waiting here all night? This is devil's work, not God's...'

But God's work was none the less for him, since Saladin's troops, having hammered at the garrison all day, were too exhausted to continue all night, and aware that Richard's ship lay at anchor awaiting reinforcements from his fifty galleys and unable to attack until he had sufficient men-at-arms, they took a well-deserved rest. Saladin, knowing that Richard's fleet was on its way and that the king could do nothing until more of his equipment arrived, sent Bohardin with a small body of troops to capture the citadel and deal with its inmates.

Richard, as yet, had no certain knowledge of the desperate plight of the garrison, but a priest who, because of his habit was allowed to pass the gates — since by mutual agreement neither Christian nor Muslim priests could be endangered — gave warning to the king by swimming to his ship at anchor in the harbour.

Hauled aboard dripping wet, he panted, 'Sire! Hasten! The bloodthirsty Turks threaten to massacre all women and children as well as the men who refuse to surrender the garrison. They will kill all the captives!'

'Not by the Sultan's orders, I'll swear to that!' cried Richard. 'I know the Sultan is merciful to the weak and defenceless. But

I will go now at once and see for myself what these Turks will dare to do, against the Sultan's orders!'

Throwing off his armour and unheeding the entreaties of his knights to let them go instead — 'Not you, Sire! You cannot go unarmoured!' — he plunged into the sea.

'All who can swim, follow me. Do not wait for the galleys. Come! To arms! And shame to him who lags behind...'

None did, but one of them had the sense to fetch the king's battle axe, for he was swimming to the shore with no weapon, not even his shield for protection.

Fortunately the Turks had not seen the king's ship approach. They were too busy pillaging the house of some of the Knight Templars who lodged in the town; and as the ship gained the shore in the wake of the king, Richard up to his waist in water waded to the beach followed by his knights and men-at-arms, all who had been with him in the royal galley, even to the ship's cook.

Soaked to the skin as he was, Richard gave the order: 'Barricade the shore — here on the land side of the harbour. Find anything — driftwood or wreckage. We must hold back Saladin's army for he'll send troops to enforce a surrender.'

Then, as the men of the garrison saw that the king's ship had landed and knew he was leading his men to their rescue they took heart, and when Richard's fleet following had disembarked their crews of knights, foot soldiers and horsemen, with the king's splendid charger, they realised they were saved...

The Turks, caught between two fires as Richard's men and those of the garrison charged down upon them, took flight, powerless against his surprise attack. The captured were now the captors.

The streets ran with blood from dismembered limbs and mutilated bodies. The Crusaders, vengeful for the intended massacre not only of the men of the garrison but of their women and children, showed no mercy to those who fled before them.

It was all over within two hours and Richard, though still unarmoured, suffered little injury, but his horse Fauvel received his death. Richard knelt beside him in the blood and sand, unashamedly sobbing, his tears dropped on the satin smooth neck stretched out in its last dying breath.

'My faithful ... I would it were myself, not you.' Then, as a riderless horse galloped past, he sprang up, seized the trailing reins, mounted him and was off racing after the routed Saracens, but he gave up the chase when he saw they had taken refuge in the mountains. 'The women and children are safe, God be thanked,' he cried.

After the rout and the capture of the garrison Richard pitched his tent outside the town, which was rapidly becoming infested with typhus due to the wholesale slaughter that left heaps of unburied dead rotting in the streets. Thankful for a respite after those few exhausting hours, he rested, but not for long.

Saphadin, the Sultan's brother in charge of the mamelukes, sent his chamberlain, Abu Bekr, to visit Malek Ric and, if possible, to arrange the peace terms that had been held up. Abu Bekr spoke and understood some English, and when he arrived with an escort he found Richard ready to welcome him.

Sherbet and the Turkish edibles so dear to the Muslim palate, and so revolting to Richard, were offered to the visitors. When Saphadin's envoys arrived they saw the English king, who had been decently clothed and cleansed by his servant after the battle, was chatting amicably with some of Saladin's mamelukes. Aided by his Syrian interpreter the chamberlain heard Richard half tauntingly say to the gratified assembly, 'That Sultan of yours is truly admirable. I have a great respect and affection for him, but why, when he sighted my galley, did he run away? I know your Turks and men of the captured town were making merry in my Templars' house and that they had looted some of their valuable belongings but why, in God's name, did he retreat at my very landing? I didn't come prepared to fight, I only wanted to talk sense with him!' Then, turning to Abu Bekr — who must have reported all this to Bohardin, who would record it — 'Greet the Sultan from me and beg him to let us have peace. My country needs me. I must leave my work here and go where I am most wanted.'

Abu Bekr was in too much awe of the English king to attempt the suggestion that peace terms could not yet be satisfied either by his Sultan or the Illustrious Malek Ric with, as it were, a scratch of the pen. Instead he bade a regretful farewell to His Highness, thanked him profusely for his gracious reception, and said he would convey to his Commander, Saphadin (Malek el Adi) the King of England's message. And bowing nose to knees he, with the equally obsequious emirs, rode back to report it all to Saphadin, who expressed himself in synonymous Turkish, that he was 'fed up' with the whole campaign and wanted peace as much as did Malek Ric.

Saladin, however, so disgusted at the defeat of his Turks whom he had placed in charge of Jaffa, was in no way 'fed up' with the campaign. He rounded on his brother and told him that as Malek Ric had proved determined to hold on to Ascalon as his right, 'which is mine!' thundered Saladin, 'my right, my Bride of Syria. Ruined though she is, I will restore her!'

Having let forth to his brother and the emirs, he said, 'I am as determined as Malek Ric. I will never forgive him for the rape of Ascalon. I will attack his camp in the field outside Jaffa.' But before he had flung down that gauntlet, he sent back word to Richard: 'Since you have evinced such trust in me I propose to share the land that lies beyond Jaffa with you, while Ascalon shall be mine.'

'So he sets the chequerboard to seek his revenge in another game that he may checkmate me!' cried Richard. 'Very well. I take the white and he takes the red, or shall we toss for it?'

But Saladin had no intention of resetting his chessboard to risk checkmate. When Richard's envoys brought him a message of thanks for his offer of a share in Jaffa, he renewed the request that Ascalon should be his and his alone; and if this request were granted, he would at once leave for England, his kingdom, that was in sore distress at his absence. To this, Saladin, as might have been expected, replied that it was impossible for him to give up Ascalon.

He made a long speech in his answer to Richard's envoys that the English king, his Illustrious Friend, well knew that if he left Syria the whole land would revert to him — 'To me, to whom my kingdom belongs. Moreover, I am an old man.' He resorted to tears that did not at all convince the envoys, one of whom was the English knight Augustin of London, a stalwart unsentimentalist.

'I have no longer the desires of the world,' said the Sultan brokenly. 'I wish only to remain here in my own land among my own people, and to die in the belief that I act according to the Will of Allah whom I serve. Nor,' he added firmly, 'would I deny my word to the Prophet until victory is granted to whomsoever Allah wills it.'

'Then let us see,' said Richard when this report was brought to him, 'whether Allah or our God — or the Infidel's devil — will be the victor. I, for one, must wait to pass through the gates of the Holy City, yet so soon as I have repaired the walls of Jaffa which are suffering from our siege, I am off to Europe — please God!'

NINE

'How much longer must we be kept here?' complained Berengaria. 'You,' to her sister queen, 'hear all the news from Richard's letters, but I am given nothing. What is happening to him and his Crusade? All I know or all you have told me is that he has taken Jaffa.'

'I have only just received this,' Joan answered worriedly, 'which tells me Saladin is again on the offensive against Richard, just when he thought peace was to be settled at last.' She scanned the sheet of parchment brought by king's messenger. 'He says that the king has fallen ill of the disease which is rampant in and around Jaffa, but he still will not give up his leadership of his army. He dictated this from his bed last night; he says, *The battle continues and Saladin has brought troops in seven divisions. I ordered my men on pain of death to keep their ranks unbroken and to remember they must stand firm even if it means martyrdom.* O, God!' she exclaimed, 'does this mean he is too ill to lead his men?'

'Martyrdom?' echoed Berengaria faintly. 'Does Richard want to be a martyr? Is this to be the end of his Crusade?'

'No!' Joan looked up from the sheet of parchment. 'He goes on to say — according to the scribe who writes this for him — that at the first wave of the Saracen charge they were halted by the barricades Richard had set up outside the walls of Jaffa, and that they received —' her eyes followed the closely written words — 'what seems to be, as much as I can understand of the scribe's writing, which is interspersed with Arabic — that the leading horsemen received such a — it looks like *a hurricane*

218

of arrows that their horses resembled hedgehogs with the bristles sticking out of them. That is Richard's dictation, for sure!'

'Is this all he has to tell you?' demanded Berengaria. 'And why is he not leading his army?'

'I think,' Joan said, turning over a page, 'the messenger told the chamberlain to whom he delivered the letter that Richard would write again so soon as he knows when he can come to terms with Saladin for a peace settlement. *I will give further news,* he says, *when there is more to tell.'*

'More to tell?' cried Berengaria. 'He has told you — or rather, he has told *me* — nothing! Why does he not write to me as well as to you?'

'Because,' Joan evasively replied, 'he doesn't wish to cause needless concern.'

'So much concern for me,' retorted Berengaria, 'that for all he knows or cares, I might be dead. I wish,' she added with a sniff, 'that I *were* dead, if I am to be kept in this heathenish land much longer!'

But she was not to be kept much longer in that 'heathenish land'.

After the rout of the Turks at Jaffa, Saladin during the night of 4 August made another attack on Richard's camp outside the walls of the town, already badly damaged. The Turkish cavalry moved stealthily, hoping to surprise Richard's exhausted army; but he, having received warning from one of his indefatigable spies, ordered his troops to prepare for battle.

Sick though he was, and delirious with the typhus that had struck him down along with half his and Saladin's armies, his men sprang to his command and, barely dressed, having been roused from sleep, they swept through Saladin's ranks with the king leading them. Vastly outnumbered, he won the day, and also the admiration not only of his own followers, but of Bohardin, the mouthpiece of Saladin.

'The king was a giant in battle ... his sword —' or his battle axe? — 'clove in two, from their helmets to their teeth, any of our Turks who came in contact with him. He mowed men down as a reaper mows corn with his sickle.'

In whatever exaggerated terms Richard's knights and Bohardin praised the courage and leadership of the intrepid Crusader king, the Turks no less than Saphadin may have been 'fed up' with the long-drawn-out campaign. Having failed in their attempt to overcome the Christians and in the sacking of Jaffa, they turned upon Saphadin, brother of the Sultan, for having robbed them of the victory they had thought to be theirs.

Richard, after this last crowning success, finally succumbed to the illness that was to lay him low for weeks. It is possible that because of his sickness he had been left in ignorance of the message sent in his name to Saladin for the negotiation of a peace settlement. His agreement to peace, on certain conditions, was primarily that Ascalon should be dismantled for the next three years, when the city would go to the more powerful of the two contenders. Besides Jaffa and the dependent territories, the Christians were to be allowed free access to Jerusalem and liberty to trade anywhere in the Sultan's land. There was to be a temporary peace for those three years between Christians and Muslims; after that time it would be necessary to renew hostilities if both sides were so inclined.

The truce was signed on 2 September; but Richard, to whom the terms of the agreement were read, and in the throes of the fever, denied any knowledge that he had waived his claim in compensation for the fortifications of Ascalon, as the agreement stated. Yet those who had entered into the transaction in his name understood he had given his consent to it and to all the clauses it contained.

He was too ill to argue the point, and falling back upon his pillows on the uneasy truckle bed in his tent, he told them, 'Since you, my administrators, and Saladin have taken advantage of my illness, it is no use denying that I know nothing of these points you raise. So I must abide by my words that have been given to the settlement by proxy.'

Richard had been bled until he was the merest shadow of himself, the mediaeval treatment for all ills. He was still suffering from his severe attack of typhus when peace was proclaimed amid general rejoicing throughout Islam, in the cities and market places of Christian and Muslims alike.

Saladin ceaselessly enquired after Richard's health and sent not only his own physician to attend him but gifts of fruit and flowers and snow to cool his fever, and seemed to be as pleased with the terms of the truce as Richard was not.

When the height of the fever abated, the king, not too ill to fly into one of his tempestuous rages, learned that many of his troops had taken full advantage of the clause which allowed them access to Jerusalem, and were already within the walls of the Holy City. 'Without me!' stormed Richard. 'I, and I alone, have the right to lead them through those gates, even were I carried there on a litter. If this is at the order of Hugh of Burgundy, let him come before me and I will deal with him as he deserves!'

But the Duke of Burgundy, to whom Richard had been bitterly opposed ever since his king, Philip Augustus, had deserted the Crusade, and — as Richard guessed — was always stirring up trouble and thwarting his commands, had also fallen victim to the typhus and lay at death's door.

When Richard was informed that Burgundy was dead, he exclaimed, 'There goes the last of my enemies here! I must now go and deal with those who trouble the heart of my kingdom.'

Saladin, however, who had rejoiced with his Muslims at the terms of the truce, now had doubts, so he told Bohardin, as to the wisdom of having made even a temporary peace.

'I do not know what may arise from it, nor if I shall live to see the renewal, if any, of hostilities. Should the enemy decide to strike again, they could increase their forces and recapture those lands we have taken from them. I fear Islam will be destroyed, since this English king — this undaunted Malek Ric — will never be content to rest if Jerusalem is not entirely in his possession. The whole reason for this, the Third Crusade, was to destroy utterly the Muslim claim to what he calls his Holy Land. It is no more holy to him than to me!'

His doubts were soon confirmed by a message from Richard that he had only asked for a three years' truce to make it possible for his return to his own land and set to rights there what had gone wrong under the interference of his brother. When he had put all to rights in England, he would return with enough men and money to liberate the entire kingdom of Jerusalem and take unto himself the lands that were the inheritance from their Saviour who died on the Cross for them.

To this, Saladin, ever chivalrous, replied that were he to lose Jerusalem he would lose it to Malek Ric rather than to any other prince in Western Europe.

The Sultan's misgivings must have been a premonition. After having drawn up the terms of a peace only for a specified time of three years, Saladin, the great leader of the Muslims, died. He had lived to unite his Islamite world in resistance to

Western aggression, and above all to maintain a lasting friendship and admiration for the English king, Richard returned him a wholehearted respect for a nobility of character he had not thought to find in the man he had known as an 'Unbeliever'.

The king set out on his journey to Haifa on 9 October 1192, eighteen months after he had led the Third Crusade to the partial success of his hopes.

Many at that time marvelled, not at the so-called 'failure' of his pilgrimage, but at its ultimate success. At the expiration of the three years' truce he intended to return and bring about his final victory.

As one of the Muslim writers in the next generation reported: *So great was the fear inspired by the powerful English king, that mothers would quiet their children, and nurses their charges with the threat: If you do not behave yourselves, England will come and carry you off...* Even, as centuries later, nurses would frighten children if they misbehaved by saying, *Boney will come down the chimney and take you away...*

After the signing of the truce, Richard remained at Haifa for several weeks during his convalescence. He sent word to the two queens at Acre to let them know for the first time how seriously ill he had been, and that he wished to be fully recovered before pursuing his voyage to England. He needed to regain his strength to deal with the present difficulties at home, which, as his good Bishop Walter had said, must be his first monarchical duty. But he told them he would send a ship fully equipped with every commodity and attendants, to convey them to Europe, and so soon as possible he would follow them to England.

Berengaria, however, decided that she did not want to go to England. 'Not yet,' she informed Joan, who of late observed that Berengaria exhibited a stubborn obstinacy not hitherto in character with the 'Damozel' of Navarre.

'Not yet? Do you then intend to stay here, when for so long you have been anxious to leave?'

'Not here, of course,' replied Berengaria cuddling her kitten, now growing to a full-sized cat. 'I am going to Rome to have the honour of an audience with the Holy Father. I wish to confess to His Holiness how I have rebelled against the neglect I have suffered from my husband, the King of England since the day of my marriage when I promised to love and obey him. I neither love nor will I obey him, and no priest lower than His Holiness shall hear the confession of the Queen Consort of England.'

'Oh? So you think you will receive absolution from the Pope rather than from the king's chaplain?'

'That is my right as queen,' Berengaria replied with a shocking nonchalance that inclined Joan, as often before, to inflict assault upon the ear of her whom she inly declared was 'getting above herself'.

So much above herself that when the king's ship arrived at Acre to carry the king's consort to England with his sister and the daughter of Isaac Comnenus of Cyprus, Berengaria commanded the captain to set sail, not directly for England, but first to Cyprus. 'There I will place the child of the so-called Emperor — who, I understand, is still in prison — to be given into charge of the Governor of the island.'

'You can't give orders to the captain of the king's ship,' cried Joan, aghast when Berengaria's latest rise above herself was brought to her. 'Richard commands that you go direct to England.'

'I take command from none, not even the king, where *my* wishes are concerned,' inexcusably retorted Berengaria. 'I am going to Rome after giving Guy de Lusignan the charge of Isaac's child. Why should I have been saddled with her, and not you who are more fitted to be her guardian, as you are so much older than I? This, I suppose, is another of Richard's commands to be obeyed, as I swore before the altar, and which —' her voice rose in shrill defiance — 'I retract!'

Joan, who had held herself in, now let herself out in a long written complaint to her brother to do with *your wife's deliberate and disgraceful challenge to your authority ... Nothing I can say will make her see reason.*

But Richard never received that letter. He had already left Haifa and was on his way to the kingdom he had left to the machinations of his brother John. By the time the ship that followed after him would have delivered Joan's complaint regarding his incalculable wife, Richard and his following galleys had met with storms still more shattering than those he had encountered on his previous voyage. His crews were on their knees praying the Holy Mother to intercede for them against the wrath of God, who, it was evident, had sought thus to punish them and their king for not completing their pilgrimage to the Holy City.

After a month of that tempest-tossed voyage, the raging winds slackened to bring them within sight of Marseilles. No news of the king or his whereabouts had now been heard for near upon three months, and it was generally assumed that his ship had been wrecked and he and all his crew drowned in the savage storms they must have encountered on the high seas.

John was in his element. There could no longer be any doubt of his succession to the throne. Yet before he could be rid of the boy, Prince Arthur, whom Richard had named his heir as the only son of his elder brother Geoffrey, deceased, he must make sure that the king was dead.

But the king was not dead, although his galley had been almost wrecked in the furious storms against which the captain and his crew had so courageously battled.

Having put in at Corfu for provisions Richard learned the disquieting news that the Count of Toulouse, an ally of his one-time close friend, Philip Augustus, now his enemy, was in league with the King of France and bent upon his capture.

Prompted by the spirit of adventure, Richard, always eager for a fight, sighted three galleys. At once, supposing them to be enemy ships and as he had no more than two of his fleet following him having sent the rest of them forward to await his arrival in his kingdom, he ordered a boat to hail the vessels and enquire on what errand bound and to whom they belonged.

As the boat neared the foremost of the three it was seen that she carried a sinister flag. 'God's Blood!' cried the officer in charge of the boat. 'She's a pirate!'

Instant attack from the pirate came hard on the approach of the boat. At once Richard's ship went into action to intercept a flight of arrows with a deadly return from the crossbowmen aboard the royal galley. Then, to the surprise of Richard's crew, the pirate's captain drew near enough to trumpet an invitation for the captain of the galley that flew the well-known red flag, emblazoned with the golden leopards of England, to come aboard.

Richard, however, politely returning the pirate's request, asked what he would take to conduct his ship to the Adriatic coast. He probably decided it was better to trust himself and his galley to the pirates rather than risk being cast adrift in uncertain weather along an unfamiliar coast.

The pirate's captain (unaware it was the king who hailed him) trumpeted his reply that he would oblige the English ship for the sum of two hundred silver marks. To this Richard readily agreed, and in the wake of the accommodating pirate, he and his following galleys made for Ragusa, an independent republic.

During the furious storms Richard had vowed to God that were he delivered from the perils of the sea he would build a church wherever he should be brought safely to land.

Led by the pirate ship, the king and a company of knights landed at a small island about a mile off the shores of Ragusa. The chief inhabitants of this island, Lacroma, were a community of Benedictine monks. The rulers of Ragusa, having heard of the king's arrival on the island at once offered him the hospitality of a lodging in their city. Richard gladly accepted their generous welcome, but in accordance with his promise to God that he would build a church wherever he landed, he ordered the church to be built on the island.

However, the republican governors of Ragusa required the restoration of their cathedral, which was in sore need of repair and, as the monastery had its own little church, Richard said he must obtain a dispensation from the Pope to deviate from his vow.

After much ecclesiastical red tape Richard's conscience was salved by the Pope's sanction, and at his own cost he supplied large sums — presumably borrowed, since his pilgrimage had drained him of almost all his ready money — to pay for the enormous cost of restoring the cathedral and the rebuilding of the monastery church.

For almost five centuries the beautiful cathedral stood, thanks to Richard's generosity, an emblem of architectural perfection and the pride of the Ragusan Republic. It was eventually destroyed by an earthquake in 1667. When rebuilt it never attained the beauty of the original. The republic kept its independence until 1810, when it was conquered by Napoleon, but Richard's name was revered throughout the centuries as the founder of Ragusa's once beloved cathedral.

From Ragusa, the king, who could not stay to see the completion of the work he had financed, took ship on 10 December to continue his journey up the Adriatic. Here once more the weather disfavoured him. Heavy storms, to which he and his crew must have become accustomed, drove him ashore on a remote corner of the Italian border a few miles from Venice. Again luck was against him, since almost all the local magnates were either connexions of or dependent upon Leopold, Duke of Austria and the Emperor of Germany, both enemies of Richard and allies of Philip of France.

When, at last, he must have realised his danger, he sent two of his followers to ask Count Meinhard of Gorza (an uncle of Conrad of Montferrat) for safe conduct across the Austrian territory. He bade one of the messengers describe himself as Baldwin of Béthune, actually the name of one of his knights; and another William de l'Etang, representing one Hugh, a merchant, both pilgrims returning from Jerusalem.

The knight, supposed to be the merchant Hugh, offered Meinhard a valuable ruby ring. Meinhard examined it closely and saw that it bore the royal arms of England. This was obviously a careless oversight on the part of Richard, who had given his ring to de l'Etang with instructions to offer it to the Count as a gift in exchange for a free pass through Austria. He would go with the two of them as their esquire.

'But this is not your ring!' exclaimed the Count. 'It bears the arms of Richard, King of England, purported to be the murderer of my kinsman, the Marquis of Montferrat. Yet since your king has honoured me with this costly gift, although I cannot receive it, I will grant you, his servants, safe conduct.'

De l'Etang, seeing that he and his fellow knight were discovered, protested that indeed they were not servants of the king. 'We are both pilgrims from the Crusade, but never attached to the king's army.'

'It is of no account,' was the suave reply. 'Even were you in the army of the king, I would not withhold your pass through Austria. Nor do I hold the King of England in jeopardy as the murderer of my nephew since so many have believed him to be. Go, then, in peace.'

When this news was brought to Richard, he ordered horses to be procured at once for him and the two knights.

'I do not trust this Meinhard,' he told them, 'he is too glib. He has hoodwinked you! He'll be after me, I'll warrant. I'll make for the Carinthian Alps, our easiest route to the frontier. He hopes to capture me before we reach Freisach.'

Meinhard had indeed hoodwinked the king's men by leading them to believe that although he knew them to be servants of the king, he would allow them safe conduct. By these means he could give warning of their approach to the frontier by sending word to his brother, Frederic of Pettau, while he himself went in pursuit of the king and his followers.

Richard, with a company of a dozen or so, set off in the middle of the night, the king disguised not as an esquire but as a Templar. When Meinhard and his men went in pursuit they captured eight of them, but Richard and three or four others escaped.

Meinhard sent word to his brother at Freisach to be on the watch for the king and his company, and above all to seize the king.

Now it chanced that Frederic had in his household a Norman named Roger who had been in his service for the last twenty years. He bade this man search the house that lodged the pilgrims and the king. If the prize were captured, Frederic promised Roger, whom he trusted implicitly, that he would give him half the town.

Roger, however, though he had not seen the present King of England for more than twenty years and had been in the service of Richard's father Henry II, penetrated his disguise and would not betray him. He begged the king, 'Sire, I beseech you for your life to lie here until nightfall. There is no moon, and you may get away unseen. I beg Your Grace to forgive me for leaving the service of the late king, your father, but that was before you were my king. I will procure excellent horses for Your Grace and your servants, that will outspeed all others.'

Richard gave him his hand. 'God bless you for your loyalty. As to the horses. I have — I *had* a favourite horse that no horse could overtake, but I —' his voice broke — 'I lost him. He fell under me at Jaffa, shot through his gallant heart in the last crowning battle of my pilgrimage.'

Back went Roger to his lord and told him that all rumours concerning the English king were lies. Although some of the pilgrims were lodged in the houses he had searched, the king was not in any of them. 'I would have recognised him,' he said, 'for I served his father, the late king, as Your Honour knows, and I knew the present king as boy and man when at the late king's Court. He has made his escape, my lord; and he will be over the border unless you follow him at once. He has a horse that none other, not even my lord's own can outspeed.'

Frederic flew into a rage. 'If what you tell me is false I'll have you hanged. But if it be true that he has got away I'll not rest until I have captured the English king who is the purported murderer of my kinsman, Conrad of Montferrat.'

The Norman blustered it out. 'My lord. Yes! May I hang — you may torture me, hang me, disembowel me if what I tell you is false. Would I betray you, my liege lord for whom I forsook the Plantagenet King Henry to serve under you? I am a Norman. My ancestors were born in the reign of England's conqueror William of —'

'Enough!' Frederic interrupted impatiently. 'I trust you, and will follow after this Richard of England now. No horse of mine but can outspeed any of his! And I will take you with me, that you may recognise him in whatever disguise he assumes.'

Roger bowed in humble acquiescence. 'If I may suggest that my lord lose no time to follow after the king, who will take his way to the border across country.'

He knew that if he sent Count Frederic off at once Richard would still remain hidden, disguised in his lodging, and at nightfall when Frederic and his men were speeding in the opposite direction Roger knew the king, under cover of the moonless night would be over the border before dawn.

While Frederic and his men were galloping far from the way Richard would take some hours later, Roger was urging the Count, 'Make all haste, my lord, while it is yet daylight, and you will seize the English king before sundown!'

Richard, with three knights and attended by a page remained in the house at Freisach. When the short December day closed in under the curtain of night, Richard and his knights mounted the horses Roger had procured. He bribed a fellow servant to bring them to a place where there could be no chance of interception until Richard and his four, including the page, were well away.

Riding three days and nights without halt, they came to the outskirts of Vienna. Still in Austrian territory, but too exhausted to go farther and aware that they could not yet be pursued, they rested before resuming their way across the border. They lodged for the night at a rude inn two or three miles from the city. Next morning to pay for their rooms Richard sent the page into the town to change some money, for he had spent what he had brought with him of Austrian currency and required enough to carry him over the border.

Unfortunately the lad could speak and understand a few words of German, and began to brag to the Viennese of his rich master who was staying in the village nearby and would now be going to Italy. But Richard, far too weary to resume his journey that day and believing Frederic had been led astray and that he was now safe from pursuit, decided to travel on the morrow if sufficiently rested. His illness had taken toll of his strength and he knew he could not continue the long journey to England until he felt strong enough.

The next day he sent the boy back to buy several bottles of wine and more appetising food than the inn could provide. Laden with his purchases, and riding one of the horses Roger had obtained for the king's escape, the foolish lad, again boastful of his 'rich master', had borrowed a pair of the king's gloves; but as these were too large for him he stuck them in his belt.

At once he was suspect by one of the citizens since Frederic, unable to capture the king when following a false scent, had on his return to Freisach advised the whole countryside to watch out for the English king or his servants.

It happened that Leopold, Duke of Austria, whom Richard had offended the year before, was in Vienna. He ordered the lad to be seized and tortured unless he would tell his captors the whereabouts of his master.

At first the terrified boy remained dumb, but when threatened to have his tongue cut out unless he would speak, and already beaten almost unconscious, he blurted the name of the lodging that housed his king. At once Leopold, elated at this so long desired capture of the man who had insulted him by removing his standard from the walls of Acre, led a company of men to the king's lodging. The boy who had betrayed him was dragged, half-dead, behind the horse of the officer in charge of the company.

Leopold bade them raid the house that the boy might indicate who was the king. 'He is sure to have disguised himself,' said Leopold.

Hearing the clatter of their approach Richard told his knight Baldwin, 'Find me a servant's habit, or the cook's — anything!' Baldwin hastily took the cook's apron, his tunic and a soiled cloth to cover his king's tell-tale red hair.

When Leopold's men stormed into the hostel with the page bound in chains between two of them, they went from room to room but found no sign of the king, only servants and the innkeeper, staring agape. Then into the kitchen they went with the page in a faint between them, and the frightened servants fled, leaving only the cook turning a capon at the spit.

'Have you not seen the English king?' shouted one of the officers, prodding the page with the hilt of his sword. 'Speak! Answer me — or die!'

He brandished the sword above the youngster's head, at which Richard, tearing off the cloth that bound his hair, sprang up from his stool. The capon on the spit fell into the fire with a sizzling smell of roast meat.

'Let be!' he cried. 'I am the King of England, and I surrender so you spare my servant's life. Release him and bring your duke to me, but first — release the boy!'

They seized the king and bound with ropes him who had saved the lad's life at the risk of his own. The page, bleeding, bruised and battered, fell on his knees before his king, sobbing and praying forgiveness for having led to his betrayal.

''Tis I,' said Richard, 'who should ask forgiveness of you whom I thoughtlessly endangered when I sent you among a horde of —' his eyes flashed round at the soldiers — 'of barbarians!'

At this moment Leopold burst into the kitchen demanding, 'You, Ricardus Rex! Put up your sword.'

'I carry no sword,' replied Richard with contemptuous cool, 'but for this present only, until I replace it with my battle axe to fell you and yours —' another scathing look — 'in righteous combat.'

'You will never meet me in combat, Richard, since you will pass the rest of your life for what it is worth to me and the Emperor and to Philip —' his sneering mouth spat the words at him — 'your well-beloved, who may care to visit you in the fortress that is prepared for your reception.' And to his men: 'Away with him!'

Baldwin and his fellow knights now rushed at the men who held Richard in vain attempt to wrest him from them.

'At your peril,' shouted Leopold, 'do you interfere with justice! You will accompany your king to share his life, or what is left of it — but not with him. No royal state for you and less for him whose Lion Heart has played you false! Go!' to his men who had seized the knights, 'we waste the daylight hours and you have a long journey before you.'

At Dürenstein, a remote castle high on a mountain overlooking the Danube, watched day and night by guards, in a noisome dungeon lay the captive king. A week after his imprisonment, Philip of France received from the Emperor of Germany the triumphant news that 'The foe of my Empire and the disturber of your Realm will trouble you no more!'

TEN

The news of Richard's capture was received by John in joyful expectation of the throne. If the king were or were not to be released, his death, as John believed, must be a certainty, for it was unlikely Richard would survive either in or out of prison. 'Not if I know it!' John told himself.

In alliance with Philip of France, John had taken every opportunity to keep Philip's hatred of Richard at boiling pitch and at the same time to foster the bitter ill-feeling of Leopold of Austria against his fellow Crusader.

John was well aware of Leopold's triumph in having captured the enemy and that he had influenced Henry VI, Emperor of Germany, to realise how much he owed *my Dearly Beloved Cousin*, as Henry described Duke Leopold in his letter to Philip, *who has taken into custody one guilty of Treachery and Mischief to me and to My Holy Roman Empire.*

The Mischief and Treachery of which Richard was alleged guilty had not been clearly defined, but Henry of Hoheushaufen was as much obsessed by the desire for European dominion as a twentieth-century Kaiser or maniacal dictator. Nor would his 'Dearly Beloved Cousin' in his turn surrender to the Holy Roman Emperor his coveted prize unless for a goodly financial reward.

At the court of Ratisbon on 6 January 1193, the royal prisoner was brought before the Emperor. Leopold, acting on the advice of 'Evil Counsel', as one Austrian chronicler had it, asked for a postponement of the trial in order to produce further evidence, and ordered Richard to be thrown back into prison.

Philip, delighted at the news of Richard's capture, sent word to Leopold to keep the 'Disturber of his Realm' in close confinement until further charges could be brought against him to be heard at a formal trial. He then conveyed a message to Richard declaring war against him and his kingdom, and followed up his threat with a letter to the Emperor offering him vast sums of money to keep Richard imprisoned for life, or else to deal with him as a traitor to himself and to the Holy Roman Empire ...

All these letters and messages, which took days or months to deliver and receive replies, must have kept Philip too busy to wage immediate war against Richard. Not until the Emperor Henry VI wrote promising to deal with the miscreant 'as he thought fit', and as he had always dealt with traitors to himself and his empire, did Philip invade Normandy.

Then John, on his knees to Philip, paid homage to him whom he also regarded as his 'Dearly Beloved'. Hands were clasped, kisses exchanged, and John in highest hopes of his ultimate kingship journeyed to Paris. There he completed his subjugation to Philip by swearing he would seize all Richard's Norman and Angevin possessions, along with the promise to take for his wife and future consort Philip's sister Alais, whom his brother had so shamefully jilted. That John already had a wife did not enter into the agreement. He had long decided that when he became king he would be rid of her, either by bigamy or by her death; it mattered not which, since a king could do no wrong...

All this was excellent. Philip, in return for John's future generosity, promised to help him to the throne of England that to the two of them looked to be a certainty. John, highly satisfied with these diplomatic relations which would establish a lasting alliance with Philip Augustus as his brother-in-law, returned to England so soon to be his kingdom, and gave out that his brother was dying.

As this prognostication did not at all convince John's would-be subjects, since none had more than his word for it, he found himself in something of a quandary. To ensure his succession he collected an army of Welsh mercenaries — for only a few of the Welsh would believe in the king's approaching death — and he also attempted to raise troops from the Scots. Again he was thwarted.

William, King of Scots, sworn ally of Richard, would not consider such traitorous suggestion. Having sent some of his own knights in support of the Crusade, he let John know what he thought of him in no mean terms, for which John swore to take his revenge when the crown was on his head.

Having to rely on an indifferent body of Welshmen to support him, as none of his brother's faithful subjects would do so for they loathed him as much as they loved their king, John occupied Windsor — and then, with his Welsh, mostly peasants and no knights or nobles, he marched to Westminster. There in the Great Hall of the Palace he proclaimed, 'The King is dead ... long live the King!' and raised not a cheer from the assembled knights, barons and those of the king's Court, who had all to do to refrain from seizing his brother and carrying him off to the Tower. 'At the best,' they muttered among themselves, 'he is mad, at the worst a fratricide.'

John had reckoned on the fealty not only of the justiciers left in charge of the kingdom, but of the king's subjects. Confronted by an indignant refusal to consider him as the king's successor, the justiciers consulted the Queen Mother.

She, as furious with John for his treachery as were the officers of the State, sent two abbots to Germany in order to discover exactly where Richard had been imprisoned, or if he were alive or indeed dead.

Richard greeted the two abbots with warmth — one of Boxley in Kent, the other of Robertsbridge, a Cistercian House in Sussex — and was thankful to learn from them all that had happened in France, England and Normandy since his incarceration. They were shocked to find him in a miserable, dark, rat-infested dungeon; the barred recess high up in the stone wall gave little light; and no view of the beauty without of the glorious river winding between the mountains. Richard laughed at their dismay.

'I have a friend here,' he said, 'or friends — the mother of a family of rats. They sing to me at night. But I have not much food to give them for such as I am allowed I cannot spare. Yet I am better cared for than my knights and the boy, little more than a child, whom they caught and brought here with me. They are in chains, and I fear they have not even a crumb of black bread offered to their festive board!' He made light of it, ignoring or feigning not to see their tears, and begged them, 'Be sure to tell my mother I am well and in good hands. My guards often come and sit here on that —' pointing to a three-legged stool on which stood a jug of water — 'and we play at chess — at least one of them has learned the rudiments of the game, and so I pass the time. Also I have composed a poem or two ... they allow me parchment and a pen and ink!'

While he grieved for what they had told him of John's treachery he, always indulgent of his brother's weaknesses, excused him by saying, 'Our young John is not one who would seize another man's right nor his kingdom. He would always bite off more than he can chew! Nor would he ever combat my right to the throne in his favour. He would never willingly injure me. As for proclaiming himself king, he lives in a lifelong fairy tale. In many ways he has never grown up. He is still a boy...' (He was twenty-seven.)

'As a boy,' said the Abbot of Robertsbridge, when they mounted their horses to take them on the return journey, 'who delights to catch spiders and pull off their legs for his pleasure!'

When the two priests arrived back in England with the news that the king was alive and well, while they refrained from reporting to the anxious mother how wretchedly her son was lodged in his damp rat-ridden cell, they relieved her anxiety to some extent, but did not prevent her from persisting in every endeavour to obtain his release. But before this encouraging news had been brought to her by the two abbots, she heard from Berengaria that Richard still lived.

The young queen consort, then in Rome, had seen in the window of a shop the jewelled belt which Richard presented to des Préaux when he had saved the king from the Saracens. The belt she had given to Richard as a wedding gift must have been stolen from des Préaux, for how did it come to be on sale in a shop at Rome? Unless the king were dead and his belongings looted.

She had heard no news of her husband, and as Joan had returned to England leaving her in Rome, Berengaria, never more than a wife in name, had now a secret longing to be reconciled to her husband. She had told Joan she intended to be received by the Pope, Celestine III, and to him she poured out her troubles and the bitter disappointment of her marriage; on the advice of His Holiness she must strive to regain her husband's love.

Having made up her mind to seek him, she began preparations for her journey to England and was waiting to hear from her father who would send a ship to bring her to her husband's kingdom.

King Sancho may have been greatly relieved to know this, for although she had never told him of her unsuccessful marriage he, who knew something of the alleged preference of Richard for his own sex, might have guessed at the reason for the failing of his daughter's married life.

She wrote to Queen Eleanor that she had seen her husband's jewel-studded belt in the window of a shop in Rome, and her mother-in-law wrote back to tell her of the disaster that had befallen him. Whereupon Berengaria urged her father to supply her with immediate transport to England.

Queen Eleanor, writing anguished letters to the Pope, begged him to rescue her son from his enemies, and in a state bordering upon hysteria she sent him a prayer she had written to the Holy Virgin: *O, Mother of Mercies, look upon a wretched mother that thy Son, the Fount of Mercies, shall punish the enemies who invade my son's dominions...*

She began to despair that her prayers and entreaties went unanswered when on 23 March Richard was conveyed from his prison at Dürrenstein to Speyer, charged with a formidable list of crimes including the rape of Cyprus, the imprisonment of Isaac Comnenus, the murder of Conrad Montferrat, finally ending with the gross insult offered to Duke Leopold of Austria by the wanton removal of his standard from the walls of Acre.

This was obviously the long-stored grievance which Leopold had waited to avenge. It had come at last in so black a list of charges that would mean death to the criminal king.

Richard's defence, conducted by himself, was a categorical denial of all accusations of which he stood accused. He spoke quietly with none of the histrionic emphasis many an experienced advocate would favour in stating his defence. He declared he had been wrongly and mistakenly charged with crimes he had never committed. Regarding the conquest of Cyprus he affirmed he had been prompted not, as was said of him, by avarice or ambition but to rid the human race of a tyrant and usurper, Isaac Comnenus. As for the Duke of Austria, if he believed he had been insulted he should have taken steps at the time to avenge an insult so long forgotten, and not waited to bring it against himself with other alleged offences.

His detention in a dungeon not fit to house an animal, much less one whose rank had been recognised in his own kingdom as superior to none but God, was a greater insult than that which the Duke of Austria thought fit to hold against him. A buzz of clamouring opposition to this cool announcement came from among the assembled knights and nobles of the Emperor's Court.

Disregarding that, and also the loud approval of the king's knights and bishops — among whom was his faithful Hubert, Bishop of Salisbury — Richard proceeded: 'I refer now to the assassination of Conrad, Marquis of Montferrat, of which I stand accused. The murderer of Conrad, when captured and sentenced to death confessed with his dying breath to have been guilty of the murder. Moreover, it is not I who am brought here on the false assumption that I failed to drive the Sultan of Islam from Jerusalem. It was the King of France and his vassal, the Duke of Burgundy, who died of the disease that laid me low, and —' his finger with the ruby ring upon it pointed at Leopold, Duke of Austria, who appeared visibly to wilt under the flashing eye of the Crusader King — 'and *you!* Yes, you, Leopold, who with your allies falsely accuse me of murder.'

He again addressed the Emperor. 'I would have you, Henry Hohenstaufen of the Holy Roman Empire, know that these three princes shamefully deserted the Sacred Cause to which they were committed and left me to fight single-handed against Saladin, the Sultan, whom I respect for a nobility of character that I find lacking in those before whom I stand to be judged … It is said that I led the Crusade for love of ambition and monetary gain rather than for love of God. Yet what have I received from my conquests? Financial reward? *No!* I swear before my Lord and Saviour whom I serve and will serve Him until my death, As for monetary gain, I possess nothing but the ring I wear; yet I am rich in the service of my Saviour who has suffered me to live that I may return to His Holy Sepulchre and redeem the Cross,' his hand strayed to the crucifix suspended on a golden chain upon his breast, 'for which I am honoured to fight. And I ask you, Henry of the Holy Roman Empire, that justice be rendered to me you accuse of crimes brought against me by my enemies, of which before the God I serve I swear I am innocent!'

He spoke with a convincing sincerity that many who had come to condemn him were overcome. Some of the more emotional of his supporters, the Italian and Norman crusaders, were in tears. Then the Emperor, perceiving that Richard had won the sympathy of the court, changed suddenly from the judge ready to pronounce the ultimate penalty upon the accused for murder, agreed that there had been some mistaken charges against the 'noble prisoner', and undertook to effect a reconciliation between the King of England and the King of France, and gave him the kiss of peace.

Richard in return promised the Emperor a hundred thousand marks as reward for his generous verdict. How he could have obtained so vast a sum when, on his own admission, he possessed nothing but the ring he wore, was not questioned. The Emperor, in tears, possibly simulated, declared that if his arbitration proved to be unsuccessful, he would be satisfied with no ransom at all, and moreover would present the 'much maligned king' with fifty fully equipped galleys and two hundred knights to conduct him back to England.

Richard, in joyful belief that he would soon be free to return to the kingdom he had left too long, at once wrote home to his mother to send him robes of scarlet and gold with furs for himself, also suitable garments for his entourage, since the wars had bereft him and them of suitable clothes.

During Easter week he -was lavishly entertained by the Emperor and given state apartments in Henry's royal palace. But the Emperor, who had shown such sudden unaccountable friendship, did as suddenly change. Without any warning, and while he still enjoyed the comfort and luxury that for so long had been denied him, Richard was again taken into custody.

His capture this time was conducted with ceremony, the officers of the Emperor supplied him with a horse, although he had no sword since he had been deprived of armour, and none of his own servants or knights was allowed to attend him, he was taken, politely, to the fortress of Triffel on the highest peak of a mountain, said to have been built only for detention of traitors to the Empire.

Now no more pretence of homage was offered to their royal captive, but the rough insulting usage they would have dealt to the lowest felon. At which Richard turned violently upon his captors denouncing 'your lying treacherous master of hypocrisy and of the devil's unholy empire!'

One of his custodians raised a fist to strike him, but his arm was stayed by another. 'Not you — not us! The Emperor will deal with him as he deserves!'

They backed to the door of the dungeon to which the king had been dragged. If his previous prison cell, as he had told the court, was unfit to house an animal, this was deplorably worse.

As the door clanged shut with a rattle of chains and the creaking of locks, Richard stood, hands so tightly clenched that his nails dug in the flesh of his palms to draw blood; and releasing his bitten underlip he uttered a cry that to those who heard it through the fungus-damp walls of the dungeon, sounded like the roar of a wounded beast.

Then words rushed from him in a hoarse cracked voice. 'You, Henry! And you, Leopold! You think to trick me with fair promises — and you — you craven Philip! You will live to regret this, for as God is my witness, you have sinned against His Word made Flesh and against me who have fought for His Cross…'

He sank to his knees on the stone floor covered with the stinking excrement of former victims and the droppings of rats; and with clasped hands he prayed: 'Lord, my God, forgive them for they know not what they do, as you forgave your murderers when you died on the Cross for them and me…'

So soon as the justiciers heard of Richard's capture following his trial in which judgement had not yet been passed, they sent the Bishop of Bath to negotiate with the Emperor for his release. This did not appear to have had any hopeful result. The bishop was not allowed access to the Emperor but only to one of his representatives. Nothing of the king, or in what prison he had been confined was known, for shortly after his removal to Triffel he had been taken to a fortress in Worms, to conceal all knowledge of his further captivity.

According to accounts from a chronicler of the time, Richard denied his jailors the satisfaction of seeing him rebel against his wretched conditions. His gaiety of spirits, whether assumed or not, allowed his rough warders to take rude liberties with him. In return he would tease them, joke with and bribe them to buy drink for him with the few pieces of money he had upon him when first captured. His idea was to make them drunk while he drank with them, but always careful not to take too much, for he thought if they were partly insensible he could rifle their pockets and find the keys of the door. This was not to be. They were never too far gone to lose their guard of him under pain of death should he effect an escape.

However, while his jailors dozed he managed to write poems, the only one of several describing the agony he suffered in that dungeon. It came into the possession of his sister, whose son Henry accompanied Richard on his Crusade, and whom he made nominal King of Jerusalem. One verse in free translation sums up the poignant theme that runs through all its verses. We have no other evidence that the king rebelled against his wretched fate more than these addressed to his sister, Countess of Champagne.

There is no English, Norman, Poitevin, Gascon,
Who has not the meanest friend for company
In such a lone forsaken prison house
As this wherein I dwell. Yet
I reproach no friend nor foe
Who not for ransom's sake will let me go...

All the world knows the charming story that has been floated into legend of the troubadour Blondel, favourite of Richard, and who, hearing of the king's capture, determined to seek him throughout the Austrian Empire.

He wandered through Austria for the fifteen months the king was in captivity, including the time he had been kept in close confinement at Dürenstein on the Rhine. Blondel would halt under the windows of every castle, so the romantic story gives it, singing the song he had composed with the king and accompanying it on his lute until at last, when he came to Worms, he heard the voice of his king take up the song and sing it with him.

The discovery of Richard, when reported by Blondel, brought about his release.

There has been some doubt as to the castle where Blondel discovered the king, and not until about seventy years later was the story written by a Frenchman who had heard the tale told that at the court of Richard there had been a *trouveur* — a traveller of some renown — one Blondel des Nesle. It is fairly certain that the originator of the romance decided that the troubadour who found the king in an Austrian castle must have been this very Blondel. The story gained credence through the ages, and is possibly all that is remembered by every schoolboy of their hero King Richard, *Coeur de Lion*.

When Eleanor the Queen Mother, rejoicing to hear from her son that he would shortly be released, she set about to provide the necessary robes for his triumphant return to his capital. Her joy was short-lived, as Hubert Walter, and other bishops and knights who had attended the trial, brought back the calamitous news of the Emperor's deception and a renewal of Richard's imprisonment. None knew where this would be, for the bishops had only learned of his further capture after they had left for England.

The distracted mother, who had prayed the Pope to rescue her son, now believing that His Holiness had failed her, wrote indignantly to tell him: *The Kings and Princes of the earth have conspired against my son, the Anointed of the Lord. One keeps him in chains, another ravages his lands...* She accused the Holy Father of not keeping his promise to send help to her son, and ended with an accusation that the Holy Father had merited the poor opinion of his people.

A daring and inexcusable approach to His Holiness, that were it any other pontiff than the gentle, tolerant Celestine, might have caused her excommunication. But the Pope, who intended to excommunicate Leopold for implementing the imprisonment of a brother Crusader and had chastised Philip with a like threat, was in an embarrassing situation. If he excommunicated Leopold and Philip he ought also to excommunicate Henry, whom he knew to be guilty of the imprisonment of the Crusader king, but he could hardly excommunicate the Holy Roman Emperor! Nor in these circumstances could he deal so severely with the Queen Mother ... So after sending a tactful message to the distraught Eleanor, assuring her he would endeavour to right the wrong that had been done to her son, he left it at that and did no more than repeat his threat to the two other culprits.

John was now in great alarm, having learned that agents in England were collecting funds for the ransom of Richard's release. Not only the nobles, barons and bishops, besides the wealthy merchants, the abbots and priors of the monasteries were also subscribing to have their king restored to them. Then he too began collecting funds for an army with which to fight his brother should he land in the kingdom John had for so long envisaged as his own.

He let himself believe that Richard was not his father's son, aware of their mother's various lovers in the past and her imprisonment for infidelity, John may have fathered a wish to the thought that should he not succeed in ousting Richard from the throne, he might attempt to prove him either the misbegotten son of his mother, or bastard son of one or other of his father's women.

Determined by any means, fair or foul, that he would attain the throne of England, John lost no time in acquainting Philip of his intention and found him equally eager as himself to deprive Richard of his kingdom. Between the two of them they decided to approach Henry the Emperor who, they understood, had begun to regret having stated he would release Richard on receipt of a suggested ransom, and was demanding a higher sum than was originally proposed.

Spurred by the fear of Richard's impending liberation, the precious pair offered the Emperor a tempting increase of the sum agreed by Richard that greatly appealed to Henry's passion for money. He, like Philip, was the son of a great king and had come into his kingdom too young to care for anything other than all that his inherited wealth could provide.

When the offer from Philip of 50,000 marks and John of 30,000 was suggested to Henry, he agreed to prolong Richard's captivity until the Michaelmas of 1194. By that time the two of them hoped to have become joint masters of Richard and his lands, while John was more than ever hopeful of the throne.

Henry, out for as much as he could bleed from them, now held out for still more than the 80,000 already offered. So enchanted were they at the prospect of success that Philip raised his sum of 50,000 to 100,000 and John his 30,000 to 80,000 marks — and never mind how they could lay hands on such vast sums, so long as they could lay hands on Richard and all that he possessed!

With Richard's kingdom almost in his grasp and the crown almost on his head, John could afford to be lavish with his bribes to any who would serve with or under him. Supported by Philip who had little enough with which to finance him, for he had ever been a spendthrift and was in debt to Richard for monetary help at the beginning of their Crusade, John sent a clerk, one Adam of St Edmund's, to approach those few of the castles in England whose barons were likely to favour a King John rather than a King Richard. This Adam, a needy clerk in holy orders, was instructed by John to hold any of the barons and nobles, to whom he managed to gain access, in readiness to bring the country under Count John's subjugation when monarch.

Adam assured the astonished — and in many cases horrified — noblemen (who believed that a lunatic had gained admittance to their castles) that there was only one king, John Count of Mortain, who had the right to wear the crown!

This Adam, who seems to have been as besotted as his master, had managed to scrape acquaintance with Hubert Walter, appointed Archbishop of Canterbury by the Queen Mother at Richard's request in reward for his faithful service to the king.

Hubert welcomed him, realising that by tactful probing and liberal libation, he could loosen the tongue of Adam to divulge more than he was ordered to tell.

'My Lord Count John, the king's brother has p-positive — *hic* — proof —' the archbishop's wine was beginning to affect the sliding tongue of Adam — 'that my Lord John's father, the king, im-p-prisoned her — the queen for having borne the late king a son not King Hen-er-y's, she having other sons — not his. King Richard is — *hic* — not the king's son!' triumphantly babbled the drink-sodden Adam.

'This is indeed a remarkable — um —' the archbishop gestured to a servant to refill Adam's goblet — 'most interesting intelligence.' Hubert was hard put to it not to order the immediate arrest of his guest for high treason along with his treacherous master, John. But as a man of God he had to tell himself to bide his time and leave just punishment to his Saviour who had bade his disciples, 'Judge not lest ye be judged...'

However, Adam's wine and the archbishop's time brought in its own revenge. His Grace having sent a messenger hot speed to London in advance of Adam's arrival in the capital, ordered the mayor of London to seize all Count John's letters carried by Adam when he should arrive at his lodgings.

This was done, and Hubert's conscience eased that he had allowed the tale-bearing clerk to leave his palace unmolested. He left the arrest of Adam to the mayor who summoned all bishops, earls and barons then in London to read the letters the mayor now held as evidence of John's treachery.

When they were shown John's treasonable designs the Council of the Realm decreed that he be deprived of all his English lands and castles.

Then, and at the command of Hubert, Archbishop of Canterbury, the bishops, abbots and members of the clergy were assembled in the chapel of St Catherine at Westminster to pronounce sentence on Count John and all his supporters as 'Disturbers of the King's peace and his Kingdom...'

Henry may have regretted he had agreed to that offer of an increase in the ransom of 180,000 marks, as promised him by that hopeful pair John and Philip, for the release of Richard. He saw that to keep him in prolonged captivity until the

251

money should be paid might mean he would never receive any money at all!

· If he let Richard go free now, he would have to rely on England's king to refund him the huge sum promised by those two for he realised that all the wealth of England's nobles, bishops and monasteries would be Richard's for the honour of having served their Crusader king and that neither John nor Philip could together raise anything like the money of their offer. But as it was too late now to withdraw his agreement he must abide by its result.

On 4 February 1194 Henry announced to the King of France and Count John, would-be King of England, that Richard would be released, despite furious protests from the two, who believed they had been tricked by Henry.

Since Richard would now have the wealth of his kingdom behind him, the Holy Roman Emperor decided it were better to deal with the devil he knew than the devils he didn't. And so the gates of the prison were thrown open to send Richard out under imperial safe conduct to Antwerp. There he was met by his joyful mother and an equally joyful army of barons and nobles, who had followed Queen Eleanor to witness the happy reunion between mother and son.

Before pursuing his journey up the Rhine Richard sent a message to Henry of Champagne and other nobles to tell them he was free, and that 'If God would avenge him of his enemies and grant his peace and forgiveness, he would, in God's good time, join them in Jerusalem to fight against the heathen and defeat him!' It was evident he intended at an early opportunity to continue his Crusade.

The Emperor decided it was in his interest to support Richard, who was more able to gratify his passion for money, than either Philip or John, now that England had had her king restored to her. He therefore wrote to Philip and John commanding them to deliver all they had seized from Richard during his captivity. By these means Henry could rest assured he would not be the loser by Richard's liberation.

At Cologne, Richard, with his mother and his suite, were lavishly entertained by the Archbishop who was only too happy to receive him in his palace under Imperial orders; and on the third day of his visit Richard attended Mass. The service took place on the feast of St Peter in Chains, and Richard declared: 'I now know of a surety the Lord hath sent his Angel and hath delivered me out of the hand of Herod...'

The comparison of the Emperor to Herod, albeit not intended, may have occasioned some offence. However, all the nobles and delegates heartily welcomed the English king and when he arrived at Antwerp the same enthusiastic reception was given to him by the subjects of the Holy Roman Emperor.

Henry may have experienced alarm when he realised the complete submission of his Imperial vassals to his late captive, since he sent word (this according to an English chronicler of the time) that the King of England must be recaptured and returned to prison. Whether this command was ever heard is not known, but we have it that *On 12 March 1193, some six weeks after his release from prison, Richard landed at Sandwich'*

The king had come into his own...

We may well believe that Philip little thought to see a shattering of his hope of a goodly slice of John's future kingdom to be handed to him on exchange for his sister, Alais. No wonder the King of France sent a desperate message to John: *Look to yourself. The devil is loose!*

Too late: the devil already was loose and in his kingdom, hailed with an uproarious welcome from the men of Kent thronging the shore to see his ship put into port, followed by the rest of his fleet.

The sun stood low above the horizon and lightened the sea with a cloth of gold as if the very heavens, as his devoted sailors believed to be, God's welcome to their Sovereign Lord!

So soon as he landed, the king made a pilgrimage to the Shrine of St Thomas at Canterbury to offer up thanks for his safe deliverance, then on to London for a Thanksgiving ceremony at St Paul's.

Many of the nobles who had accompanied him to England were so intent upon besieging John's castles and rendering to their king all that rightly was his, that they could not attend the Thanksgiving service. But some of the German knights who had accompanied him at their Emperor's command — probably to spy out the land of their erstwhile captive — remarked grimly as they rode through the shouting streets and saw the splendid houses of rich citizens and the magnificent mansions of the nobles with lawns spreading to the Thames, where the king's ships and barges rode on the breast of the great river, that their Emperor would never have freed the imprisoned Sovereign of England at so low a price had he seen the great wealth of the king's city! Or he might never have let him free at all!

Richard's next move was to liberate the remaining castles held by John, most of which had already been released by the king's nobles. These had gone without a struggle; but Nottingham refused to surrender, John having won the castle with promises of ample reward for loyalty to him when in the near future he would become their king.

While Nottingham refused to give in, Richard set up a gallows under the walls, and pitched his camp near to the castle seized by John. Several of Richard's men were killed in the successful fight for it.

The king then hanged some of John's men-at-arms as traitors for having fought against their sovereign; and later, when rested after that engagement, he dined unattended by his knights in a private room of the castle.

There, believing Richard dead, and knowing John proclaimed himself king, the constables of Nottingham sent envoys to pay their respects to 'King John'. They had learned of the battle at the castle gates and that several of King John's men had been killed by the loyal men of the late King Richard.

'Who is it you are come to see?' demanded Richard, holding the leg of a capon and tearing at the roasted flesh with his teeth.

The envoys knelt. 'We come from the constables of Nottingham, Sire, to see and to welcome the king.'

'Which king do you wish to welcome?' Richard asked, casting aside the gnawed bone and taking another.

'Which king do you wish to welcome?' Richard asked.

'The — the king, Sire,' stammered one of the two, in a state.

'Well,' Richard began on the second bone, 'you see him.'

Both rose to their feet. 'The k-king?' stuttered the other, in a stare.

'Do you think I'm his ghost — or what do you think?'

'S-Sire,' in pitiable confusion, the first envoy managed to say. 'We were told — that — the king — King Richard — is dead!'

'So you see King Richard now — very much alive!'

The two fell again on their knees. 'Sire, forgive —'

'Go on! Up with you! Go back to your masters and tell them your king. King Richard, is not dead! But first —' he gestured to a servant — 'bring another flagon and sit you both of you, and drink — to the king!'

They got to their feet, red as a couple of turkey cocks. 'God be praised,' feebly said one of the pair; and seated on the stools brought forward to the table, they lifted their goblets and with one voice, more articulate now, called a toast to 'The king — King Richard, God bless him!'

They were not the only men of Nottingham to God bless King Richard. When the constables heard that the king was indeed alive they came, accompanied by twelve others, and flung themselves at the feet of the king, who received them with good cheer and more copious toasts and God blessings.

The next morning, having slept off the enthusiastic welcome from the constables and men of Nottingham, Richard decided to visit Sherwood Forest which had been his father's hunting preserve. He hoped to encounter Robin Hood of whom he had heard so much and was interested to see and hear for himself if he who robbed the rich to give to the poor was in truth the famous outlaw whose name resounded in the ballads of the day.

Always eager for any new adventure he told the knights in attendance to wait for him some distance off in the forest, and proceeded to disguise himself in the habit of an abbot he had ordered a servant to bring. He then proceeded on foot to search for and meet the alleged Robin Hood with his band of 'merry men'.

Whether this meeting actually took place is uncertain, and may have had its origin in the early Plantagenet folklore of a woodland sprite named Robin, who eventually became mortal as the Earl of Huntingdon, according to the unlikely tales told of him. But because Richard, on reclaiming the throne dispensed with the barbarous penalty exacted by the forest laws of castrating and blinding any caught poaching in the royal preserves under the rank of a knight or clerk in Holy Orders, we may believe that the meeting between 'Robin Hood' and King Richard did take place, as recounted, under a greenwood tree in Sherwood Forest.

We may also believe that the worthy abbot was presented to Friar Tuck, the obese and jolly monk who thoroughly enjoyed the haunch of venison he poached, and that Richard enjoyed what was offered him no less; and that he made acquaintance with Little John and the rest of them, and drank of the goodly wine with which the feast was laced. But this jollification does not seem to have prevented Richard, upon his restoration, from again somewhat inconsistently enforcing the savage game laws.

Then, barely three months after his return, Richard determined to continue his vendetta against Philip Augustus, for he had no intention of remaining in England indefinitely. He must also ascertain how far John had been involved in his attempt to possess himself of the kingdom. But before he could confront John with his treachery he would have to satisfy those of his subjects who had been gulled in believing him dead. News travelled slowly in those leisurely Plantagenet days, and in the counties not a hundred miles from London many men of the shires thought that the king was either dead or still a prisoner somewhere in Germany. He therefore decided to be publicly recrowned and acclaimed king throughout his realm.

This, a second coronation, dated back to an old English custom obsolete since the year 1157, of wearing the crown on every public occasion. After conferring with the Archbishop of

Canterbury, Hubert Walter, his faithful friend and counsellor, Richard sought finally to repair the damage done to the rightful sovereign by John's incalculable mischief.

With all due solemnity Richard's second crowning was conducted at Winchester. Magnificent in his royal robes, the crown on his head, the sceptre in his hand, and preceded by a procession of bishops, earls, abbots, monks and all the clergy with William, King of Scots and his knights — including, doubtless, the valiant young redhead the A'Hannach, Richard knelt to receive the benediction from the archbishop.

Watched by Queen Eleanor and her women in the north transept of the cathedral, there may have been some giggling asides between the ladies prompted by the ubiquitous Ambroise, who had never been long absent from the king on any spectacular event, whether it were warring in the Middle East or in the Monarch's peaceable England.

'He should have two heads,' murmured the irrepressible Ambroise, 'to wear a double crown...'

When Richard returned to his apartments in Winchester Castle, he at once set about assembling his fleet at Portsmouth to sail for Normandy. And at last, weather permitting, with an abatement of recent storms and gales, Richard sailed for Barfleur. As usual, his mother came too.

It has been remarked that the king's queen consort was conspicuously absent at this second coronation, as was also the king's sister. She, who had left Berengaria in Rome, went on to Aquitaine, which she had always felt to be her home, rather than Richard's kingdom of England.

When Berengaria learned that her husband had been restored to his throne and recrowned, she made all haste to be in time for his second coronation. Unfortunately she found that her father, King Sancho of Navarre, was dangerously ill and his physicians doubted his survival.

He died a week after she arrived at her father's Court. Torn with grief, she was left to attend to the funeral arrangements, while her brother Sancho, heir to the throne of Navarre, had invaded Normandy with intent to deliver Richard from his enemy, Philip of France, who was attempting to possess himself of all Richard's Norman domains.

There was much speculation among the king's subjects as to why the queen consort had lived apart from her husband, the king, for these — how long? — four years? As she had deserted her wifely duties as consort — so catty feminine gossip may have had it — he could have engaged in extra-marital consolation during her sojourn in Rome. She was received by the Pope there, and possibly received other less eminent persons in their turn.

But now the interest of the nation was centred, if not on the absence of the queen, on the king's determination to pursue his feud against King Philip of France. Richard left England after his second crowning in May 1194 and landed at Barfleur in pursuit of him who had been more than a friend and was now his sworn enemy. His landing was met with tumultuous rejoicing from young and old who had suffered from the ravages of the French king and his satellite, the hopeful King John.

When all the jubilations at the king's landing were over and, as was said, scarcely one sober man remained in the town to tell the gladsome news, Richard went on his way, still with no sign of his queen. This does not seem to have disturbed him, since he had all his favourite knights and devotees in his train.

Meanwhile Philip had been hard at it besieging Verneuil, with John safely in the rear of the French armies, knowing that were he seen by the men loyal to his brother it would be the end of him and the crown he still wishfully thought to be his. But at the approach of the forces King Richard had mustered — all thirsting for the blood of Philip of France to avenge the wrongs he had done to their Sovereign and themselves in his desertion of the Crusade — Philip took flight.

John fled after him in fear of Richard's host announcing its approach with shouts and trumpet blares and all the warnings of battle. Philip was not risking his life, or the huge indemnity Richard would demand of him were he spared to pay for his deliverance, any more than would John, in pitiable fright afraid to meet the brother he had so treacherously betrayed. He knew that his mother, the indomitable Eleanor, would not be far from Richard in his latest venture to seek vengeance upon Philip and regain his rights, even if it meant war to the death against the King of France.

John was right.

Eleanor had accompanied Richard to the Court at Caen where, as usual, she did the honours at the reception the king gave to his faithful bishops, barons and all who delighted in his return as it seemed from a purported grave — the prison where, so John let the world believe, the king — his brother — had died. To Eleanor he sent a message to grant an interview to her 'penitent and erring son'.

Eleanor had not hesitated to let her 'penitent and erring son' know her opinion of him during his malicious campaign against his brother. Although never her favourite, she knew, with a psychological insight rare in a woman of the Middle Ages, how jealousy of his brother had possessed out of all reason the mind of this youngest spoilt darling of his father who, not until he lay dying, had realised his son's inherent treachery. So did his mother make allowances for John.

To her presence he was admitted. She offered him no encouragement to speak; surrounded by her women she sat in stately silence.

Deprived of speech, his knees shaking, his face grey with fear of 'this terrible old bitch', as he mentally described her in the equivalent vernacular of archaic Norman French, he stood until after a prodigious effort he brought himself to utter the words forming on a dry tongue that tasted suddenly of lemons.

'Ma-Madame, I am come to ask if you w-will —' he swallowed — 'of y-your clemency to — to intercede for me...'

'To intercede with whom and for what?' croaked his mother, her hard gimlet eyes fixed upon him as if to bore holes.

'W-with Richard,' blurted John, 'who holds against me all the wrongs.' He was gaining courage now that he could tactically lay to others the mischief done to Richard — not by *him*. 'The wrongs,' he repeated, manufacturing tears (he was always adept at producing a lachrymal effect) — 'that Philip of France did in causing Richard's wickedly unjust imprisonment and his alliance with Leopold of Austria to accuse me' — he began now to believe in his innocence as the victim of Leopold, and Philip, and was bordering on hysterics — 'to accuse me of *their* evil ... *I* have done no wrong ... It is I who am betrayed!' He sank to his knees, covering his face, and watched between his fingers the effect of this upon his mother.

'Get up!' she commanded. 'Why come to me with your complaints? It is Richard of whom you must ask pardon for the wickedness with which you have been victimised by those two hell-hounds who have sold themselves to the devil. Take yourself and your whinings to Richard. He will deal with you as you deserve — and may he show you more clemency than I who wash my hands of you. Go!'

He staggered to his feet, and she, turning to her women, ordered, 'Take him to the king's chamber, and give him over to the guards at the king's door.'

Richard indeed showed more clemency than did 'that terrible old bitch' his mother. With the loss of his castles, his revenue and all the wealth John had stolen from Richard, it was an abject 'John Lackland' who came sobbing, genuinely tearful this time, and cast himself at his brother's feet.

'P-pardon me, brother, my k-king,' he stuttered. He had a slight impediment, not quite a stammer, in his speech, of which he made good use when angling for sympathy, to find favour with women, or when intent upon a conquest.

Richard stretched out an arm to him. 'Come, John, don't be afraid that I will do to you what I am waiting to do to your allies who, like a couple of vultures, have swooped down upon you — a poor little sparrow — to pluck out your feathers and then fall upon and eat you alive!' This with a snarling show of teeth and a growling voice so that John — terrified of the awful fate that Richard mischievously suggested would await him if he again fell victim to the snares of those 'two vultures' — prostrated himself.

Richard raised him. 'You need not fear that I will eat *you*! Would I devour a child? You have never been a man. You don't have to ask pardon of me. Those two who have beguiled you with fantasies of my kingdom and my crown — it is *they* whom I'll devour! Come, then I'll eat ... no, not you — you idiot!' And to his attendants, 'Bring me that fresh salmon I caught at dawn today.'

The salmon was brought, and John, recovered from his fright, was regaled by his brother at the table spread with a sumptuous repast.

But John never regained any land he had stolen from Richard, even the castle of Evreux that Philip had given him was taken back by the king. So he was 'John Lackland' again.

ELEVEN

Berengaria left Navarre several days before Richard's second coronation and was journeying to England, unaware of recent events in her husband's kingdom, and of the renewal of hostilities between Richard and Philip of France.

The heat of the July sun made the going intolerable over rough-hewn roads from Navarre and to Richard's Angevin empire, halting wherever a possible inn could be found to accommodate her and her suite.

She travelled part of the way to Angoulême in a litter, but always considerate of her servants she chose to spare them the discomfort of the stony sun-baked tracks, and abandoned the litter for a carriage. This was a conveyance used only for royalty or the nobility, and despite its luxurious upholstery was devoid of springs and little better than a cart on wooden wheels. The two windows, where the heavy curtains had been drawn back for air, served only to increase the sweltering heat and caused the queen's elderly attendant, who had been her governess, a moustached and dour-visaged virgin of fifty, to fall in a faint.

Berengaria called a halt, applied restoratives from her vinaigrette and, ordering a groom to bring a horse for her to ride pillion, she consigned the unhappy lady to her maids to be carried in a litter.

As they pursued their journey another delay halted them. This time a courier who pulled up his sweating horse a few yards from Berengaria, who was riding pillion behind her groom on a powerful black mare, one she had often ridden at home in Navarre when she used to follow deer hounds with her brother Sancho.

She recognised the courier as one of Sancho's equerries when, baring his head, he bowed low from the saddle.

'Madame — Highness. I come from the king, Your Grace's brother, who bids me tell Your Grace that should you advance into Normandy you will be in danger from the war that King Sancho and your husband King Richard are waging against the King of France and Duke Leopold of Austria.'

'What, then?' cried Berengaria. 'Am I to return to Navarre when I am halfway to the coast of Normandy? And if my brother and the king, my husband, are at war and in danger, I will be there beside them. Am I a coward to run?'

The same impetuosity that, since her childhood, if ever her sex were invoked to guard her in conventual isolation from the pursuits of man, was again asserted to bid the courier who, no less than his horse, was in sorry case, having ridden at top speed from the battlefield often pursued by a rain of arrows.

'Go! And follow behind my train. My servants will provide you with a fresh horse and will care for your poor beast. I see you too are in sore need of rest and refreshment.' And to her men, 'On through Normandy! I go to join the two kings, my husband and my brother...'

The hazardous march led by the queen aroused the admiration of all, and the concern of her doctor, who feared she would exhaust her strength. However, she insisted on going on, while news given at each halt told her of the bitter fighting between Poitou and Angoulême. She also heard from her women, who had it from the men entertaining her brother's emissary, how Richard had come to the aid of King Sancho and his band of Navarrese at Tours.

After a furious battle Sancho's small army had been all but overpowered, and was about to surrender to Philip's murderous onslaught when Richard, arriving with his Norman hosts, battered at the walls of the fortress at Loches on the outskirts of Tours, seized the castle and released the exhausted knights and men within it.

'My brother!' cried Berengaria, one of her women having brought her news of the battle at Tours. 'What of him?'

'Sancho the Strong,' as his men named him, she was told, 'is unharmed, and joins with King Richard. Together they lay waste to the land from Poitou to Maine. The battlefields are strewn with the bodies of the dead, English, Norman, French, and the Navarrese. The very air rains blood,' recounted the queen's maid of honour, enjoying this sanguinary *histoire*.

'Silence,' commanded the governess as the pale Berengaria covered her ears against more horrific disclosures. Then — 'On!' — the queen raised her head and kicked her heel into the black mare's side; and her groom, unprepared for the sudden leap forward of his mount, almost lost his seat. 'We must make all speed that I may join my brother and the king, my husband. As for you,' she admonished her groom, '*you* had best ride pillion behind *me* if you go to crack your nose on the mare's neck when she jumps!'

'Madame,' the quaking old governess called from her litter, 'I implore Your Highness to return to safety! I cannot allow you to —'

'Who dares allow or not allow me? On to Rouen,' again she bade her followers, 'or wherever the battle for right and justice is fought. I will be there with my husband, the king, and my brother. And those who fear the sight of blood — go hide your eyes and leave me to it!'

In a matter of weeks Richard had regained all his Norman and Angevin territories, stretching from the Channel to the Basque country bordering Navarre.

Philip at first put up a pretence at defiance with the threat of fearful counter-attacks that would defeat not only England's king but the whole of his kingdom from Dover to the Scottish border. Richard, hearing of this bluster, jeered at it, saying he was ready for any attack from the French king. Calling his favourite knights to his tent, they made merry on the good wine of Angoulême. *The city which,* he wrote triumphantly to Archbishop Walter, *we took in a single evening, and the armies we have captured number at least three hundred knights and forty thousand men…*

No wonder Philip quailed at the thought of meeting Richard in another battle royal; and instead of attacking, the French fell into retreat. Philip hid himself in a church off the main road to hear Mass where, in sanctuary, he knew he would be safe.

Richard rode on in pursuit of the retreating French until his weary horse dropped dead under him. By this time Philip had had enough of it, especially as his ally Leopold, who had taken little part in the present war against Richard, now threatened he would put to death all hostages he held unless Richard handed over to him his young niece Eleanor of Brittany (the child Prince Arthur's sister) in marriage to Leopold's son.

Anxious to secure a wealthy marriage for his niece, and as Leopold had settled his old grievance against the English king over the removal of his standard from the walls of Acre, Richard agreed, and the Princess Eleanor journeyed to Austria in the care of Richard's knight, Baldwin of Béthune. Richard had evidently thought that should his nephew Arthur become king after his death, he would find an ally in Leopold, his own erstwhile enemy.

But this was not to be, nor was young Arthur's destiny kingship; John would see to that. Nor did Leopold have the satisfaction of holding his hostages until Richard handed him his niece. It was on the road to Austria that Baldwin and his young charge were met with the news of Leopold's death. An awful death, by all accounts, and which the loyal adherents of Richard believed to have been God's punishment for the imprisonment of their king, a brother Crusader, to bring about Leopold's excommunication.

During the Christmas festivities Leopold had taken part in the general rejoicing at the Birth of Christ, including a tourney, in which his horse fell and crushed his foot. Little was thought of that, more than a sprained ankle, but apparently a bone had been broken and gangrene set in. No doctor was available, and none dared amputate the foot. Finally his chamberlain undertook to wield a mallet, which failed to sever the bone. Then Leopold, mindful that if he died he must die excommunicated and would go to hell for a certainty, himself struck the blow that severed the foot, yet the gangrene had already eaten into the bone, and he died in agony.

According to Hovenden, as imaginative a gossip as Ambroise, God's vengeance on Leopold for his evil misdeeds was not satisfied with his promise to release the hostages he held as penance for his sins. The Wrath of the Almighty had caused the cities of the Duke's domain to be consumed by fire, the Danube to overflow its banks and the crops to swarm with worms, presumably to devour the body of Leopold, burning in hell. Baldwin of Béthune, horrified to hear of these cataclysms, and joyful at the death of Leopold — never mind how or for why — at once returned his young charge, the Princess Eleanor, to her uncle Richard and that was the end of that — and of Leopold.

Berengaria, on her way to meet her husband and her brother, learned that Richard had fallen seriously ill. Mindful of God's vengeance upon Leopold, not only in his loss of a self-amputated foot and its deadly result, but in the devastation of his cities and his crops, Richard determined that if *he* should die in his bed — and not, as he hoped, on the field of battle — he too must ask forgiveness for his sins.

It happened that a week or two before his illness (which may have been recurrent malaria, contracted in the Middle East but unknown to the doctors of his day) he met with a hermit while out hawking at Poitou; a second time he had encountered a hermit, and of which he at once took advantage.

This holy if insanitary man, in his verminous rags, bade him solemnly beware of the Wrath of God and be mindful of the fate of Sodom, which gave Richard fearfully to think. While feverishly tossing on his camp bed outside the walls of Poitou, he believed that God's Wrath was already manifested in his illness and that he must make immediate amends. He recalled how, in the words of St Luke, one penitent brought more joy to heaven than did all the righteous men.

He summoned his priests, and in agonised self-abasement confessed to the neglect of his wife and his preference for war and bloodshed rather than duty to his kingdom. He carefully avoided more than a cursory confession for his love of men rather than of women — in particular Philip Augustus, King of France, whom he once had loved as a David for a Jonathan, and was now his deadliest enemy. He begged forgiveness for all his mortal sins, and prayed he would not be damned to everlasting.

He received absolution, and for penance, as before, was bidden to take his wife to him as her husband and to worship her for better and for worse, for richer or for poorer. But the worship of her body was omitted, or not demanded, in the marriage service of the Middle Ages.

His conscience salved and, recovered from his illness, he resolved to approach Philip with the offer of a truce. He had no doubt Philip would be willing to comply, even if for a temporary respite from continuous bloodshed and the loss of his territories and armies.

Realising that Richard's recovery from his illness and his resolution to amend his ways had made a new man of him, that he was no longer the warrior king intent upon the confiscation of France and the destruction of him and his forces, Philip emerged from sanctuary confident that now he need have no fear of reprisals. Buoyed up by Richard's professed desire for peace and goodwill to all men, Philip was again ravaging Richard's lands and causing havoc among the English.

This, instead of bloodthirsty revenge, brought from the reformed Richard a pacific compromise with the decision that teams of two champions should be elected with five combatants on either side, the tourney to take place in public. Both Richard and Philip were to be among the five in judicial combat.

Philip, well aware that he was no match for the powerful Lion Heart, called off the match, and the fallacious truce proceeded with sporadic raids between the armies of the two kings in which Richard chose to remain aloof, no longer a sinner but a would-be saint.

Since his confession and absolution for his besetting sin of which the hermit had warned him, it was remarked by all that the king was a reformed character. He attended daily Mass, kept all days of Holy Obligation in prayer and penance, visited the sick, gave alms to the poor and restored to the churches the gold and silver he had taken to pay for his ransom.

Meanwhile Berengaria, pursuing her long, wearisome journey, heard of Richard's illness, though not yet of his recovery.

It was a very different Richard from the husband Berengaria had left four years before who greeted her return, if not as a lover, rather as a magnanimous parent welcoming a prodigal daughter.

As she knelt to receive his chaste kiss upon her forehead with the words, 'All is forgiven you, my child,' she may have wondered for what she was forgiven. The desertion of a marriage that had never been a marriage? Or had she been at fault in taking leave of him without permission? She could at least be thankful for the homage she received as Queen Consort, even if her husband regarded her as daughter rather than as wife.

She now, for company, had his sister Joan who, since Richard's release from prison, had taken up her residence with him. And from her Berengaria heard of Joan's betrothal to the Count of Toulouse. This had been arranged by Richard who had fought against the Count, the father of young Raymond Toulouse, with the stipulation that not only should his son marry his sister, but that he should supply the Duchy of Aquitaine with five hundred men-at-arms if required, for a continuance of war with Philip of France.

As for Berengaria, Joan expressed herself delighted that she had been restored to Richard, and attempted to extract confidences concerning the relations between the king and his queen on her return.

'I understand from Richard,' Joan tactfully fabricated, 'that he did not expect you here yet, and has not been able to redecorate the apartments he had planned for you and your suite in time. Which is why you have separate bedrooms.'

'We have always had separate bedrooms,' was all Joan got from that.

She tried again. 'He is overjoyed to have you back.'

'Oh?'

'Of course. He adores you. He was saying only yesterday' (Joan prayed God was not listening to this whitest of lies) 'that you are more beautiful than ever.'

'Oh?' with repetitive lack of originality.

'He said you are like a beautiful boy. I mean —' Joan hastily amended — 'being so much younger than he, and so childishly formed.'

'Like a mental deficient, or one of his pages?'

'No — as if,' Joan was blushing dreadfully. How difficult and awkward Berengaria could be! No wonder Richard fought shy of her. 'As if he could not think of you as anything but the loveliest and most intelligent … there has never been any other woman in his life but you,' Joan achieved, this time with conviction.

'That I can believe,' was said, with shocking nonchalance, as Berengaria turned to take a sweetmeat from a dish on a stool beside her.

'I wonder at you!' Suddenly Joan's patience exploded. 'You have never seemed to realise that you are married to the greatest king in Christendom!'

'So great that he cares for nothing but to fight against Philip of France since he left off fighting for the Cross. How rightly it was said of him that he loves Mars better than Venus. As for sharing his bed, since you are dying to know whether we do or we don't, well — we don't!'

'I didn't — I mean —' stammered Joan. *Good heaven!* she thought. *What has happened to the girl?*

'As for sleeping with Richard,' Berengaria helped herself to another stick of marchpane, 'I'd as soon sleep with a eunuch for all the use he would have of me.' And reflectively she munched.

To Richard Joan complained of his exasperating wife. 'I greatly fear that Berengaria has found another to — to engage her.'

'To engage her?' Richard raised a tawny red eyebrow. 'To engage her — how?'

'Oh, to hell with the pair of you!' cried the vexed Joan. 'You're as bad as she is — or worse.'

'What on earth,' Richard, puzzled, protested, 'have we — have I — done?'

'It's what you *haven't* done!' said Joan, and left him wondering.

Christmas 1195 was celebrated with little festive cheer, since Richard's conversion to a life of peace and goodwill to all men had caused him to pass this Birthday of the Lord in prayerful contemplation and thanksgiving. There was some music and singing from Blondel and, at the king's request, a hymn composed by himself. There was no dancing, but garlands of flowers and laurel were permitted to deck the heads of the young men and girls. Richard sat with his sulky-mouthed queen beside him at the head of the long trestle boards in the great hall of the castle, and permitted liberal flagons of wine to be passed.

It is likely that Ambroise may have nostalgically remembered other Christmas Days that, if less holy, were more joyful, when he recorded:

They danced till the last hours
Their heads bedecked with flowers
And drank until matins had rung
Then homeward made their way among
the harlots ...

Berengaria also may have recalled a Christmas Day in Rome when she and a charming young cousin, the son of Philippe of Flanders who had been killed in the Holy Wars, danced till all hours and walked to Midnight Mass hand-in-hand through the moon-lighted streets. Their attendants, discreetly following at a distance under the starlit sky, had nodded with indulgent smiles for the young queen and the young prince who, after Mass, in the dawning made their homeward way, she to the palazzo where she had been given apartments by His Holiness, Pope Celestine, and he to serenade her beneath the window he thought to be hers, but which was that of the governess. (We may believe the good lady, an elderly spinster, to be greatly flattered...)

Berengaria sighingly remembered how Philippe and she had hoped to have been married when they 'grew up'. And now here she sat beside the king, her husband, who turned to ask her, 'Why so sad, my child, on this so joyous night?'

About as joyous as a death's head at the feast, was what she didn't say but thought, and said, 'Is there to be no dancing? My feet are cold on this stone floor.'

'I will have the rugs I brought from Syria to be laid for your feet,' said Richard kindly, and turning to the servant behind him he gave an order. A rug of many woven colours was ceremoniously laid, but she shook her head.

'I do not need a heathen carpet to warm me. This is a prayer rug, is it not?'

'Yes, the heathen use them for their prayers,' assented Richard, and raised his goblet. 'Let this good wine warm you, then.'

She handed her goblet to be refilled and glanced across its brimming silver to where Joan and Raymond Toulouse sat, Joan on the king's right and Raymond next to her. Berengaria watched them, heads together, mouth to mouth in whispers, lost to the company, lost to all save each other, soon to be married. And Ambroise, from his seat lower down, raised his cup to them and composed an impromptu *sirvente*:

Let lovers know nor grief nor gloom
Nor any sadness or distress...
But only joy and happiness...

Well into the New Year did Richard's conversion continue, while those of his most intimate knights began to doubt his sanity, so lost was he in his devotions, his daily attendance at Mass, his benefactions to the poor whom he ordered to come each day in all cities and villages to receive his bounty. Reminded of the outlawed Robin Hood who robbed the rich to give to the poor, he increased his alms and had a number of holy vessels and chalices made for all the churches that had been ransacked to pay his ransoms, many of which he had been unable to replace.

Yet the truce that since the previous July had been made between Richard and Philip was, on the part of France, very ill-kept even to the extent of certain 'Assassins', followers of the 'Old Man of the Mountain' who had murdered Conrad of Montferrat, seeking audience with the king ... 'For the purpose, Sire,' as warned by his officers, 'of killing Your Grace, God forbid, at the order of Philip of France.' While Richard, as the pious pacifist, refused to believe that Philip was involved in murderous intent against his person, he delayed passing sentence on the alleged 'Assassins' until more definite proof had been found to incriminate them or the King of France.

However, Archbishop Hubert, who had ever been more a man of the world than a man of God and a shrewd politician, did not take so lenient a view of this possible manoeuvre of Philip — and, as he suspected, of John — despite he had been forgiven and restored to Richard's brotherly love. And as counsellor and more or less head of the government, he gave blunt warning to the converted warrior king.

'You, so merciless and brilliant a general in leading your armies against your enemies Philip and the late Leopold, are singularly — and as I might put it — foolishly indulgent to those who plot against you. In your scrupulous devotion to Christianity, you seem to be unaware of the dangers that surround you and your kingdom from enemies you too readily forgive.'

'I endeavour,' said Richard, mildly, 'to follow our Lord's teaching when nailed to the Cross. The thief hanging beside him who asked to be forgiven was told, "this day you will be with me in Paradise."'

'I think,' was the archbishop's reply, 'that neither you nor Philip will be together in Paradise until you have been purged in Purgatory, and taken to heaven as friends of God — which is unlikely.'

Ignoring Richard's startled query, 'Why? Surely not! You must realise,' the prelate continued, 'that we live in a world a thousand years after Him who forgave sinners at a time when forgiveness was unknown to the Roman Empire, and those who were Christians were thrown to the lions.'

'Do you want Philip to be thrown to me?' Richard achieved a dismal look behind a chuckle, 'whom they name the Lion — or the Lion's Heart?'

'I want and expect you,' he was severely reminded, 'to fulfil your duties to your kingdom and your subjects, and to heed the danger signals that threaten you, both from Philip, your sworn enemy and,' he said meaningfully, 'your brother John.'

'My brother John,' said the now gentle Richard, 'is entirely submissive and repentant of his childish follies when he got himself proclaimed king at my supposed death ... I forgave him because he has always been a child, he has never grown to manhood.'

'So childish,' retorted Hubert, 'that he would plunge a dagger in your Lion's Heart as childishly as a boy would crucify a cat, for fun — as I have seen!'

The Archbishop's warning may have induced Richard to suspect an olive branch in the shape of a golden coronet, 'a very precious token of our friendship', offered by Henry Hohenstaufen of the Holy Roman Empire. He exhorted Richard by the fealty he owed his Imperial Sovereignty to invade the French king's domains with the promise to avenge the injuries done to his Imperial Self as well as to the Lion Heart, the King of England, Duke of Normandy and Angevin. He piled on the royal heritages with flattering unction that did not at all impress Richard, but rather increased his mistrust of Henry's intent to use him, not as the Lion's Heart, but as the Lion's paw!

He dismissed Henry's envoy with the ambiguous promise to consider in what manner or how much the Emperor was prepared to aid him in retribution of any injury done to him by Philip Augustus.

Philip, upon hearing of these abortive negotiations on the part of Henry, and Richard's apparent agreement with the Emperor to war against France for his own rapacious ends, decided to terminate the truce between France and England. He at once mustered his forces to contend against Richard whom he realised might no longer be in *rapprochement* with him and France, since the formidable Lion Heart was himself again and out for blood.

The two kings with their respective armies encamped on opposite banks of the Seine, ostensibly to discuss terms of peace or renewed hostilities. But already Richard's knights who were heartily sick of these indecisions and their king's religious or conscientious objections to war other than the fight for Christendom *versus* the Unbeliever, raided the Castle of Vaudreuil near to the venue intended for the peace conference.

Philip, in a great flurry, knew his only chance to save the castle would be to undermine its foundations. He ordered his men to hack at its walls, and so brought the fortress crashing to the ground.

This was enough for Richard to abandon his Christian goodwill towards men and love-your-enemies and all the rest of it. Crossing the Seine with many of his heavily mailed knights he led them with his awful battle axe, striking blows right and left upon the air, and uttering his terrible war cries, until the bridge broke and plunged them all into the river. Richard got a fearful ducking and was almost drowned. Fortunately he and the knights were good swimmers despite their heavy armour, and infuriated by the jeers and cheers of the French who had witnessed, as they hoped, the drowning of the king and his followers they scrambled up the banks of the river, fell upon the enemy and soon put most of them to flight, while Philip fled. He must have deeply regretted Richard's *volte-*

face from Christian pacifist to warmonger. It was as if after months of penance and piety he had recovered the strength, not only of his elbow that wielded his horrifying battle axe, but the might of his indomitable spirit.

Hubert Walter, with self-congratulatory complacence, watched from afar the effect of his counsel to the king to be himself again.

John, however, to whom Richard had restored his counties of Mortain and Gloucester along with his brotherly forgiveness and the advice to steer clear of 'bad company in future' (meaning Philip and his allies including the Holy Roman Emperor), also watched how that Hovenden reported the *merciless great slaughter of those who resisted the King of England's armies, entered the territories of the King of France, reaped the standing corn, uprooted the vines, burned the towns, and massacred the innocents...*

John may have wondered what reprisals Philip would take to revenge these vicious operations and 'massacre of innocents'. If continued they must inevitably result either in Richard's death (*God forbid,* unconvincingly did John pray the Almighty) or in Philip's ultimate victory, which would bring Richard in homage to France and, God willing, again John besought the King of Heaven to render him the kingdom over which he solemnly believed he would reign, to the eternal advantage of England and his future subjects.

And now yet another truce was to be arranged; the armies were to disband, and the two kings would exchange the kiss of peace. So disgusted were the knights of both kings with these alternate battle cries and kisses of peace that one of Richard's fighting troubadours, Bertran de Born, swore he would renounce his part in every war, and betook him to a monastery where he died — from what cause, unless of drink and his

279

partiality to the famous wine of the Cistercians where he became a monk — was never known.

In that same year 1195, the self-styled 'Emperor', Isaac Comnenus, also died — in the dungeon where he had been thrown after the victory of Cyprus, his silver fetters long tarnished and himself forgotten. Meanwhile, in London, the citizens had been suffering from the ever-increasing taxation imposed on them by the king to finance his wars with France.

Led by the first poor man's lawyer, William Fitzosbert, they were agitating for the taxes to be borne by the wealthy nobles, landowners and merchants, and not by themselves, impoverished and starving.

Fitzosbert, diligently striving to arouse the sympathy of the oppressive nobles, was met with the curt reminder that they acted on behalf of the king who had promised to come to the assistance of the taxpayers when sufficient money had been raised to support his armies either in war or in peace. The good Fitzosbert was also reminded that the king had continued to give alms to needy townsfolk and villagers throughout the kingdom, and also in his Norman and Angevin domains.

Hubert Walter, Archbishop of Canterbury, acting as chief justiciar in the absence of the king, summoned the 'king of the poor', as Fitzosbert was known, to appear before him. The 'poor man's lawyer' was leading a demonstration in St Paul's Churchyard to inaugurate a general uprising of the poor against the rich, when he was commanded to the presence of the Archbishop. Refusing to obey the command, Fitzosbert was arrested. His mob of down-and-outs, ragged starving wretches, and Jews who had been taxed out of existence, their houses ransacked, their wives and children with them sent adrift, attempted to rescue their leader but were overcome by Hubert

Walter's men-at-arms. The Archbishop, acting on the king's behalf, deferred judgement until he could approach Richard, whom he guessed would be lenient with the agitators.

Knowing that the king was at Poitiers pending a 'final' truce with Philip, the Archbishop hoped that the agitation would be over before Richard could attend to the appeal of the poor.

But Fitzosbert managed to escape arrest and took sanctuary in St Mary-le-Bow; yet the troops sent to find him set fire to the church, pulled Fitzosbert from the smoking pile, tied him to the tail of a horse and had him dragged to the Tower and hanged along with a few other insurgents who had not fled with him.

Thus ended the first protest known to history of workingmen against the burden of taxation and injustice until, in the twentieth century, the so-called 'rich' were to suffer far greater injustice in favour of the 'poor' than in the Middle Ages when the Rights of Government outweighed the Rights of Man and the unfortunate 'rich' were taxed as were the Jews of the past, almost out of existence.

Richard, impatiently waiting for a 'final peace', was now engaged in another row between himself and Philip.

This, possibly implemented in the background by John, whose 'childish' mischief had been too indulgently forgiven by his brother, was over the wardship of the child Duke of Brittany, Prince Arthur.

His mother, Constance, widow of Geoffrey — on whose death Arthur had become the heir to Richard's throne — had managed until recently to keep the little prince under her control in Brittany; but now that Philip had joined in what appeared to be the defiance of Constance and the Bretons to the crown, so enraged was Richard that he determined to punish the rebels in his usual way — of war.

With his army he invaded Brittany, *sparing neither man, woman nor child,* according to Hovenden.

Some of the Bretons with Constance and her child prince fled to Paris, and there, under the guardianship of Philip, Arthur was to remain until his Uncle John brought him to England — to meet his murdered end.

By this time Richard had received Hubert Walter's news of Fitzosbert, 'the poor man's lawyer', and how he and his demonstrative mob had been brought to the gallows. Richard, writing to thank the archbishop for his success in dealing with *those disturbers of the peace,* added, *I think we are again nearer war again than peace with France.*

Meanwhile, although Richard still allowed alms to be distributed among the poor, it cannot be said that the niggardly allowance offered to each wretched applicant was sufficient to feed, house and clothe them for a month, or even a week, much less for a year as the king had promised.

Berengaria, at Queen Eleanor's command, accompanied her husband on all his campaigns against Philip of France, 'because,' the Queen Mother told her, 'the people of England and of all the king's domains have been too long discussing your continued absence.' (Eleanor would, of course, blame the wife and never the husband for their separation.) 'And it is incumbent upon you to maintain the position to which, as Queen Consort, you have been called by God and His Anointed.'

'Yes, Madame,' said Berengaria meekly, and she thought, *As if His Anointed would care a godon whatever or wherever my position might be, so long as it isn't in his bed.* She had learned from the king's knights some of their vernacular, and if put to it could swear like any trooper.

'I very much doubt,' continued Eleanor, who had never accepted Berengaria as the lesser wife of two evils when he had renounced Alais of France, 'if there is any —' she paused to substitute the words *of his intimate men friends* for 'outside the court who have ever set eyes on you.'

'I regret, Madame,' said Berengaria, downcasting a glance at her thin elegant hands folded demurely in her lap, 'if I have not fulfilled my duties as the wife of God's Anointed.' *And that's quite enough from you,* she added silently, *you old cow!* (or possibly its French equivalent, *vielle vache…)*

Although Richard's alms had hitherto been distributed wherever he might be in residence while not engaged in war, the king himself never gave his bounty to the mendicants; it was usually an upper servant or the Lord Chamberlain who officiated for him. But the Queen Mother having decided that Berengaria might prove to be a useful deputy for her lord and master, the king, she was told to dispense the royal bounty.

Berengaria, new to the distressing sight of the ragged herd of beggars who filed through the great hall of the castle, sat on a throne-like chair to receive them, and it cannot be said she enjoyed her queenly duty. As each filthy hand was extended to receive from her the bagful of copper coins, none of which in modern currency equalled more than a few pence, she could hardly contain her nausea at the stench of them. Attended by her maids and the governess, with four security guards behind her, she must have wished herself anywhere but within sight and stink of the beneficiaries. Each in turn, either hobbling or if crippled, wheeled by another in a barrow while the more able, covered in some cases with sores painted on their bare skin to simulate horrific diseases; or some, to ensure sympathy, on crutches, that so soon as they were out of sight of the castle would be chucked aside — each was handed his or her dole by the queen.

The last of the file to receive the king's bounty was in better case than most of them, a buxom clean and personable woman with a boy of some six or seven years — a dark handsome child unlike many of the starvelings brought there by a parent in rags or half naked. Berengaria wondered why the woman who appeared, if not well to do at least not in need of niggardly alms, had joined these tatterdemalion petitioners.

As she curtsied to the queen to receive the bag of coins Berengaria said gently, 'I am sorry to think you, who seem so well cared for, require the king's bounty. Do you live in Poitiers?'

'No, Madame,' the woman raised her head with a look of defiance. 'I am from Chinon, where I have lived these many years in the same house beneath the castle where the late king died.'

'From Chinon? Have you walked all that distance?'

'Distance is of no account to one who is accustomed to using the feet with which they were born, having no other conveyance,' was the answer, in a tone that bordered upon insolence.

'Is this little one yours?' asked Berengaria, thinking the woman resented that she was in need of alms like any other of the impoverished.

'He is mine,' replied the woman. 'I brought him to see his father, believing he would be here in residence to distribute the king's alms.'

'His father?' Berengaria looked about her, and at the guards, as if to find him standing there. 'Who is his father?'

The woman uttered a hoarse laugh. 'One who has denied him, and were I to name the man who begot him with me these seven years gone, I'd risk my life and my boy's for treason.'

One of the four guards came forward from behind the queen's chair to murmur in her ear, exhaling a strong whiff of garlic. 'I beg Your Grace's pardon, but I would warn Your Highness not to parley with this woman. She has been seen about the town these several days spreading all kind of scandalous talk in the taverns. She is said to be wanting, if not mad. Shall I have her taken into custody, Madame? She has no right to force an entrance here. She is no beggar.' All this in hissing whispers.

Berengaria drew back from his garlic-laden breath that was almost as unpleasant as the stench of the departing mendicants. 'Poor creature! If she be mad, she must be attended by the doctor who is in charge of the household staff. I cannot permit her to be taken into custody unless she has been medically examined. She does not appear to be mad, nor wanting.'

The woman said, her tone again bordering upon insolence, 'I may be wanting, but not in the sense that man,' pointing to the guard, 'would have you believe, my queen. And as for wanting, all I want is justice and the rights due to me as the mother of my son.'

'Madame, Your Grace,' again the sergeant was at the queen's ear, 'if she be not a lunatic she is one of those rebels who caused such a stir a few weeks back in London. Only about half a dozen along with their leader were caught and hanged. I beg Your Highness to have me arrest her.'

'No.' Berengaria turned upon him sharply. 'Send for a doctor, have her brought to the servants' quarters and given food and a bed for herself and the child. I'll not have it on my conscience to condemn unjustly one who may be sick in mind if not in body. Let the doctor decide upon her condition.'

'Madame,' the governess now urged her, 'do not be imprudent, but let the guard know what is best to be done for the woman, who might well have forced an entrance on unlawful business and —'

She was cut short by the queen with an order to one of her maids. 'Go with her and the sergeant and see that she be treated fairly. Send the doctor to me when he has made a report.' And to the woman: 'Have no fear, you will be well cared for.'

The doctor, having examined the woman, when brought to the queen gave his opinion that the woman was not actually insane, but deluded. 'She demanded,' said the doctor, 'that the father of her misbegotten son be confronted as one in too high a station of life to own him or give him the due to a — she dared to say —' the doctor apologetically submitted — 'due to a royal bastard. The madhouses,' affirmed the doctor, 'are full of such who, on one point only, are deluded. But as we are short of houses to keep them unless dangerous to the community, we do not send them to an asylum. She is, I can assure you, Madame, harmless save for her insistence that the child is of royal parentage. It is obvious that unless she be under a delusion she is attempting to obtain money by false pretence. It is a risk all royal persons are put to, and in many cases without any proof or foundation.' Having thus delivered his opinion he bowed himself out.

Berengaria dismissed the incident until it recurred with something Joan told her when she came to Poitou, while her husband — to whom she had been married since January of that year — was supporting Richard again upon the warpath.

286

Philip had laid siege to Aumale, and Richard had retaliated by taking the castle of Nohancourt, where he received a bolt from a crossbow aimed by one of Philip's captains. This had laid him out for a week or two and, unable to mount a horse, he was more than ever enraged against Philip, and saw himself, despite recurrent peace agreements, condemned to indecisive war with France.

Joan, in a state of perpetual anxiety over Raymond who, with five hundred men-at-arms, was harrying Philip in Normandy, incessantly complained to Berengaria that she wished to God she had never agreed that Raymond should support Richard, if he insisted on these everlasting raids to prevent Philip from burning or destroying the Angevin castles. 'I tell you I am sick of it!' She thumped a cushion of the chair where she sat, a tambour frame before her, and a cross-bred spaniel at her feet. The dog, alarmed at the thump that he might have thought would descend on him, jumped up, entangled a foot in a skein of silk from her embroidery, and brought down upon him the tambour frame and the tapestry on which Joan was at work.

'God damn the dog!' she cried. 'He's a bastard — in every sense of the word! His mother went astray with one of Richard's prize greyhounds. There are bastards enough in our family without breeding them in our kennels!' Then, with the dog gazing piteously up at her as he strove to disentangle his paw from the silken skein, she caught him in her arms and kissed his blunt nose. 'We can't blame you for the sin of your father — or was it your mother, poor pet?'

'That reminds me,' Berengaria knelt at the fallen frame with its embroidery partly unravelled. 'Oh! Look! He has pulled out almost the whole of this stag's head. I was saying that talking of bastards reminded me of something that happened here when I was distributing the doles, just before you came. You will have to start this stag's head all over again, unless you stick him with an arrow in the hunt and make him bleed…'

'What about bastards and the dole?' asked Joan, setting down the apologetic dog.

'Nothing really, only there was a woman who stayed behind and spoke to me. The guards thought she was a lunatic, and I called a doctor to examine her. She didn't come for the money, she came to see me and tried to make me believe that the child she brought with her was a royal bastard. She couldn't, or wouldn't, say whose son he is supposed to be, but I have an idea she was trying to pass him off as Richard's.'

'Oh, yes,' Joan nodded, a smile dawning. 'I know all about *her*. Richard told me ages ago how he had been pestered for some indiscretion with a woman on one of his few visits to Chinon. She sent him a message when his father lay dying that she had to see him urgently, and showed him the child of a few months old. Of course it was all a pack of lies. Royalty has always been, and always will be, victimised by any woman — or man for that matter — who may never have met him or even seen him. We know our father, King Henry, was utterly promiscuous, and that he gave us two half-brothers whom he loved more than any one of us except John. He imprisoned our mother because of her alleged adultery — maybe she deserved it, for before she married our father she had half a dozen lovers. John is for ever hinting that Richard is not our father's son, but he has done nothing to prove the king a bastard. As for that woman who attempted to gain recognition either in money or land for herself, I'm told this boy of hers bears not the least resemblance to Richard, whose colouring — his red hair — throws back to William I, Duke of Normandy, our great-great-grandfather, whose son was William II — Red Rufus they called him, for his red hair. But this woman who has tried to saddle Richard with her by-blow has another son much older than this one, whom she named Philip ... Philip de Cagne.'

'How,' asked Berengaria, wide-eyed, 'do you know all this?'

Joan shrugged. 'How does one know or hear the babble of idlers who have naught to do but to mind the business of others rather than their own? Possibly it originated from Ambroise, or Bertran de Born, who in the past outrivalled even that arch-gossip Hovenden. Maybe before Bertran turned monk when he daren't open his mouth to the sin and slander, he gave out that she named her first born Philip — after Philip of France — so it is probably his.'

Berengaria said, with the smallest of smiles, 'I understand — for I can hear the babble of idlers too, that Richard has never had to do with any woman either before or after marriage, and not even with his wife — so they say...'

Joan bent over the retrieved tambour frame. 'Have you heard what Raymond calls you?'

'What does he call me?'

'What all men who have ever seen or met you have called you — "the desired, but never the desiring".'

'My desire is not for the love of man for woman, but for that which I can never attain. And I can't tell you what that is, for 'tis something all of us want, and can never achieve — at least in this life. Although we are created in God's image we are as far removed from Him as hell from heaven.'

Joan shook her head and cast a look, half-questioning, half-puzzled, at the little queen whose cynical philosophy was inapposite to her rebellious youth.

When Raymond returned on a short leave from Normandy, she told him, 'I do feel that Berengaria ought to ask for a dispensation to have her marriage annulled. Richard has systematically ignored her existence until he confessed his sins — or his one obsessive sin — and turned saint for a few months. She is born to be a wife and mother, not just an appendage to Richard, and of less account to him than one of his hawks.'

'She is young enough yet,' Raymond said, 'to find a man who will give her all she has missed.'

'She may,' Joan said with a private little smile, 'have already found him — when in Rome…'

'To do as the Romans do — and did,' laughed Raymond.

But Joan was soon again to lose her husband, for he joined Richard in his apparently endless and indecisive war with Philip. He had it firmly in mind that France would over-run his entire Angevin domain unless he managed to hold back Philip's advance into his territories. The difficulty with which Richard now had to contend was lack of funds, due to the heavy ransom he still had to pay Henry Hohenstaufen for his release from prison. Philip had far more resources than he with which to maintain his armies, and as the years dragged on with intermittent conferences for a truce, and renewed slaughter on both sides, Richard was compelled to call upon mercenaries until he had scarcely the means with which to pay them. It had now become a tug-of-war between the two rival kings, and with each fresh attack so did Richard's mercenaries become more demanding.

And still the raids upon the castles and garrisons of the French and English continued, with merciless bloodshed and hideous reprisals. As Richard was responsible for forty-five castles in Normandy, the defence of these, and the rebuilding and provisioning of the garrisons, drained his fast-dwindling resources. The fiercest fighting was in the Seine Valley and soon it began to look like a cemetery of unburied dead. But if Richard were forced to call on his unwilling mercenaries, he still retained his permanent knights and men-at-arms. Among these were the highly skilled craftsmen who not only built but operated the siege engines.

His chief commander, of the foot soldiers who had been with him on his crusade and throughout the war with Philip, was Mercadier. Yet while Philip could almost equal Richard as a director of siege warfare he would never meet him in pitched battle. And as time passed, interspersed with peace conferences that could result in no more than a temporary truce, it was as if both kings struggled for supremacy with no decisive victory to either.

When the French advance threatened Rouen and endangered Normandy with their superior forces, Richard conceived his boldest venture: the building of the famous castle on the rocky island of Andelys. And this despite the protests of the Archbishop of Rouen and other bishops, who were horrified at the slaughter of their priests, the demolishing of their churches and the continuous raids on the Norman castles and garrisons. Even when a deputation of the bishops was brought to the Pope, military consideration took precedence over papal edicts, and as Celestine gave no positive opinion for or against the petition of the clergy, Richard proceeded with the building of his castle under personal direction.

He intended it to be, as it finally became, the most famous castle in Europe, the Château Gaillard-les-Andelys. It commanded all traffic up and down the Seine, and would be a formidable fortress no enemy invader could pass.

To protect the indefatigable masons continually harassed by the French, Richard commandeered a host of Welsh mercenaries who fought with the same merciless ferocity and disregard of life as did Philip's men-at-arms. At least two or three thousand of these Welsh were slaughtered at the entrance to the vale of Andelys. This Richard avenged by taking prisoners captured in the fight for the castle even before one-half of it was built. Three of these were thrown down and dashed to pieces at the base of the rocky island. Fifteen others Richard sent to Philip under the guidance of a one-eyed man. If intended as a joke, it further exacerbated Philip that in reprisal he flung three of his English prisoners from a cliff on the opposite bank of the river, blinded fifteen of them and sent them to Richard in the care of one of their wives.

In the midst of the French and English making merry over this vicious and senseless revenge of the rival kings, a rain of blood was seen to fall from the sky upon the island of Andelys. All believed this phenomenon to be a manifestation of the wrath of God at the wicked cruelty of the French and English in throwing to their deaths and blinding the innocents who fought for them; but it was more likely to have been a reflection from the red-tinted clouds of the late August sunset after a dry hot summer.

It was this dry rainless heat that scorched the earth and caused a drought for loss of water from the springs, to bring upon the armies a pestilence that was said to have been imported by pilgrims returning from the Holy Land. Many on both the French and English sides were infected, and so high was the mortality that there was not enough land to bury the dead except in shared graves of both French and English.

During the necessary halt of hostilities due to the plague, as the fever was thought to be, John took advantage of the opportunity to prove himself a reformed character and, with an eye to the main chance in the hope of Richard's death from pestilence, if not in battle, he allied himself to Mercadier, who raided the castle of the Bishop of Beauvais, one of Richard's most dangerous enemies. He it was who spread the rumour that Richard had been the murderer of Conrad of Montferrat. John realised that the capture of the castle of Beauvais and its bishop would be a great asset to his exchequer when he became king, in God's good time, which he saw to be an ever nearing possibility in view of the continuous battle between the kings of France and England.

While under Mercadier's command John took to himself the honour of capturing the Bishop of Beauvais, and triumphantly returned with him to Richard. Notwithstanding his brother's heavy debts he received not only Richard's gratitude but the major portion of 5,000 marks Richard distributed to Mercadier's men who had captured the bishop.

At the king's command Beauvais was flung into a dungeon at Rouen, where he remained, and, loaded with chains, was forced to endure the ignominy of imprisonment until the next peace conference.

Within a few weeks, toward the end of September in the year 1197, Philip watched the erection of the Château Gaillard. Even his own courtiers could not refrain from expressing their admiration for the building of what looked to be a magnificent fortification.

This served the more to infuriate Philip, who saw the immense advantage to Richard would be this sturdy fortress in defence of invasion.

'I care not,' Philip boastfully proclaimed, 'if the walls are built of iron. I intent to conquer Normandy and Aquitaine, and damn Richard and his paltry mercenaries to hell!'

When this was reported to Richard he swore: 'By God's Throat, were the walls of my castle built of butter I would hold it against Philip and the whole of France!'

And still the war dragged on with indecisive battles between the French and English, while the pestilence took its toll and famine spread due to the dry summer, and crops ravaged by the fighting armies. Richard's demands for more and more money increased, and arbitrary taxation was laid upon the wretched peasantry and small land owners, while even the fees of the knights were reduced.

Dissension among the feudal lords and their dependants did nothing to lessen Richard's financial difficulties; but a victory over the French king at Gisors heartened him to declare: 'Thus have we defeated the King of France, yet it is not we, but God and my right.' *(Dieu et mon droit*, the early inception of the motto of the English Crown). Richard modestly disclaimed that his small force of no more than sixty had vanquished a French army of five or six hundred.

Hovenden, always ready to discredit Philip in favour of Richard, told how the English, who vastly outnumbered the French, had ransacked and burnt about eighteen towns and villages. Philip's army retreated in such disordered haste that the bridge over a tributary of the Seine collapsed under their weight with Richard charging down upon them, *like a hungry lion*, so Hovenden records it, *to devour his prey*.

If Richard did intend to devour the King of France, his appetite went unsatisfied when Philip fell into the river and had to be dragged out by his legs, to the jeers of the English, while at least twenty of his knights were drowned.

Richard celebrated his victory during Christmas at Rouen with Berengaria in second place to the Queen Mother. There was dancing, feasting, and an extravagance of food and drink that Richard could ill afford, yet the conquest of Gisors led him to believe he had come to the end of his pecuniary trouble, if not to the end of the war.

But the building of the Château Gaillard had depleted him of almost his entire resources. He was still in debt to Henry Hohenstaufen for more than half his ransom, nor had he enough to pay his mercenaries guarding the Norman frontier. Many of them deserted with those of his allies on whom he relied for financial help.

He wrote a scathingly bitter *sirvente* to the Prince of Auvergne.

Your aid vanished hence
When my pay ceased to flow
We've no silver nor pence
As you very well know
A rich king you would quit
Brave and faithful, to boot
But I'm miser, poltroon,
Now you've changed your tune …

He was in desperate need of cash to carry on hostilities that could only result in slaughter on both sides, with no advantage to either.

Hubert Walter, acting as Regent during the king's continued absence, negotiated with Philip in person for a peace treaty which that arch-diplomat foresaw would finally terminate this insensate war. The agreement with an exchange of oaths was signed on St Hilary's Day in January 1199, and on that day the two kings met for the last time. Richard moored a boat in the middle of the Seine, and Philip was on the opposite bank. Neither wished to exchange the customary kiss of peace, and only half-hearted cheers from both sides greeted the proclamation by a herald that the English and French armies were disbanded.

Yet it was not in Richard to remain idle, or resume his monarchical duties in England, now that neither king would continue at each other's throats. Since he could not satisfy his lust for war upon a field of battle, Richard turned again to build one more, if less imposing, castle on an island in the Seine.

The building of the château he intended to name Boutevante ('push forward') was not pushed forward very far when a diversion halted the laying of little more than its foundations. Richard had heard that a peasant ploughing at Chaluz near Limoges had dug up treasure long buried by the Romans. Because this was found on land owned by its overlord, Viscount Aimon, he claimed the right to it. Richard, however, demanded *his* right to it as the Sovereign, since property found in any part of his domain belonged to the Crown.

In vain Lord Aimon opposed the king's claim, offering him a portion of the treasure, which was said to be considerable. Richard emphatically refused, saying he would have the whole of it and, if needs must, would fight for it. Reports of fabulous wealth in gold coins, and a table of gold at which were seated an emperor, his wife, sons, and daughters, had come to the king's ears. It is doubtful if the skeletons of a purported emperor and his family seated at a table of gold (more likely to have been a shield of iron), could have benefited Richard by lessening his debts. As for vast wealth, there was certainly a quantity of coins, probably Roman, but unlikely to have been discovered in sackfuls, as reported, rather a few handfuls thrown up in lumps of soil.

However, since Lord Aimon insisted that the treasure was his, and Richard's need for money was urgent, he at once set about to storm the castle of Chaluz, with Mercadier and the few remaining mercenaries who had not yet deserted.

When Aimon realised that the formidable Richard was approaching with what he feared to be an army, and as he had scarcely fifteen men left in charge of the garrison, he fled, leaving his ill-equipped men-at-arms, some merely boys, to cope with the king's attack. Richard made short shrift of them, shooting indiscriminately with his crossbow at any man he saw on the castle's walls.

The garrison was on the point of surrender, when a youth, one Bertrand de Gourdon, shot an arrow at the king who, with careless disregard for his safety, had discarded defensive armour other than his headpiece and a buckler. For this 'child's play', as he called it, he had not brought with him his murderous battle axe, nor did he intend to take any prisoners from the small garrison. He would release them all. once in possession of the castle and most of its treasure hidden he suspected, in the dungeons or bricked up in the walls.

The boy Bertrand, whose courage all but equalled the king's and armed only with a crossbow and a frying pan for a shield, sent a bolt whistling through the air straight at Richard. The wooden shaft broke off, to leave only the bolthead. The arrow struck the king in the neck and became embedded in his shoulder.

All attempt to pull it out failed to dislodge it. Richard had put on weight in these last few months of peace, free from continuous war; and supervision of the building of yet another castle did not offer enough exercise for his abundant physical energy.

Seeing Mercadier rounding up the few remaining defenders of the castle he returned to his tent and sent for a surgeon, who was bidden, 'For God's sake get this damn thing out of me!'

Easier said than done. Night was falling and the insufficient light of one *flambeau* in the gathering dark of the king's tent where a curtained couch had been brought that he could keep within sight of the castle, made it difficult for the surgeon to extract the few inches of the iron bolthead.

Richard, cursing loudly, swore his usual oath, 'By God's Throat! If you can't get at it without tearing my shoulder to rags, find another surgeon who will!'

With profuse apologies the surgeon, assistant to the king's chief medical officer, sent an orderly to fetch his senior.

Together they hacked at the obstinate arrow-head, while Richard, scorning the agony of his lacerated flesh, roared between spasms of pain: 'Go on! Get me out of here that I may recompense Aimon for the damage to his castle.' And, to one of his knights standing by, horrified to see the blood pouring from the torn shoulder as the two surgeons cut into it — 'Tell Mercadier to cease his attack on these men of the garrison. I shall need them to show me where the — God damn! Can't either of you dig the thing out of me without cutting off my arm?'

At last the surgeons succeeded in extracting the arrow though the wound refused to respond to treatment. Laudanum was given to subdue the agony caused by the repeated tearing of the flesh, but the worst was not yet over. Gangrene rapidly set in, and Richard knew there could be little chance of recovery. None was allowed near him save four of his most trusted knights and his favourite troubadour, Blondel.

On his knees beside the couch, his tears dropping on that clammy hand he heard the king mutter: 'You saved me from prison — and — had I a sword — give me a sword!'

A sword was brought, and weak though he was, he tapped the kneeling Blondel's shoulder saying, 'Arise ... Sir Blondel des Nesle...' Then, exhausted with the effort, he lay back struggling for breath to say, 'My mother ... send...' then managed, with his fading breath, to call the boy Bertrand de Gourdon to his side.

Those who watched what seemed to be a defiance of his final enemy that was slowly, inexorably defeating him, marvelled at the sudden strength, as of a candle sprung from its dying flame, which enabled him to utter the words, stretching a hand to the boy's bent head: 'What have I done to you ... that you should ... kill me?'

Without a tremor of fear for the hideous fate the lad knew awaited him and which would mean as certain death as that of his murdered king: 'You killed my father and my two brothers.' The lad's head was proudly raised. 'And I swore to God that I would kill you before you killed me. Do with me as you will. I am content to die.' In those filmed blue eyes a flame still flickered to show a brightening spark.

'You shall not die,' the feeble voice floated on the breathless air. 'You will live to fight again, though I ... shall not be here ... to lead you. I ... forgive.'

His eyelids sank.

A sob tore from the boy, who knelt to take that flaccid hand, still warm in the last pulse of life.

Bowing his head upon it, he murmured, 'I will fight for you, and for your kingdom, now and for ever ... my king.'

AFTERWORD

It is typical of Richard's spiritual generosity that he bore no ill will to his enemies and to those who had threatened his life. He had long forgiven Conrad of Montferrat, his would-be murderer, and in those last words, 'I forgive...' he must have included the once loved Philip of France against whom he had so relentlessly fought, yet in his heart he surely never hated.

His chaplain, Father Miles, administered Extreme Unction. The king took Holy Communion for the first time in seven years, and requested he be buried at the feet of his father's tomb in Fontevraud Abbey.

When he knew his end was near he made his will, leaving a hundred English shillings to Bertrand de Gourdon whose fatal arrow killed him, and ordered that he be set free to serve under his successor. But Mercadier, after the king's death, disobeyed his command and ordered Bertrand to be flayed alive, his limbs drawn apart by horses and dragged to the gallows to die a traitor's death.

To the people of Rouen Richard bequeathed his heart in a golden casket. He desired neither his wife nor his sister Joan to be with him at his deathbed; but in answer to his message begging his mother to come to him, she came ... in time to hold him in her arms as he drew his last breath.

Too grief-stricken for tears, she may have whispered to him the words she wrote to the Pope: *I have lost the staff of my life, the light of my eyes* ...

Of his neglected wife we learn little more than that she was known as *La Reine Blanche,* not for her presumed virginity but for the white widow's weeds she wore during the thirty years she outlived the husband to whom she had never been a wife save in name. Known as the Countess of Mans, after the province Richard gave her for a wedding gift, she is said to have spent most of her life in the convent of the Cistercians at Mans where she founded the Abbey of l'Espans.

As king, Richard is given no eulogistic obituaries; but his reckless courage and his devotion to the Third Crusade is associated with his name throughout the Christian world.

As to that name known to posterity and to every hero-worshipping schoolboy, legend tells how, supposedly it originated, that when attacked by a lion he tore out its heart with his bare hands.

Reckless of danger, and of a valour unequalled by any of his contemporaries, strong and merciless in battle, knight errand to the weak and helpless, he could yet be guilty of barbarous cruelties in those dark Middle Ages.

Not undeservedly was he nicknamed by his intimates as 'Richard Yea and Nay' for his many changes of mood from heroic optimism to despairing indecision, as when he covered his eyes that he might not look upon the Holy City, knowing himself to be, at that time, insufficiently equipped to fight for Jerusalem. It was his tragedy he could not, as he, intended, fight for to conquer the city of his dreams.

Indifferent to personal danger, fearless fighter of bloodthirsty battles, he seems at variance with the aesthetic versifier and indubitably talented musician, as we are told in the legend of Blondel, who sang beneath a prison window the very song composed and echoed by the captive king and so led to his release.

Finally, as history remembers him and as Gibbon wrote of him: *If heroism is confined to brutal force and ferocious valour he stands high among the heroes of his age...*

High too in the hearts of those to whom the name Richard Plantagenet is synonymous with *Coeur de Lion.*

A NOTE TO THE READER

If you have enjoyed this novel enough to leave a review on **Amazon** and **Goodreads**, then we would be truly grateful.

Sapere Books

Sapere Books is an exciting new publisher of brilliant fiction and popular history.

To find out more about our latest releases and our monthly bargain books visit our website: **saperebooks.com**

Printed in Great Britain
by Amazon

28941076R00170